BOOKS BY AUBREY MENEN

DEAD MAN IN THE SILVER MARKET

THE DUKE OF GALLODORO

THE BACKWARD BRIDE

THE STUMBLING STONE

THE PREVALENCE OF WITCHES

Charles Scribner's Sons

DEAD MAN
IN THE SILVER MARKET

DEAD MAN
IN THE
SILVER MARKET

by Aubrey Menen

NEW YORK

Charles Scribner's Sons

1953

PRINTED IN THE UNITED STATES OF AMERICA
BY THE HADDON CRAFTSMEN, INC., SCRANTON, PA.

Chapter Two appeared in *The New Yorker*
in a slightly different form.

For PHILIP DALLAS

CONTENTS

DEAD MAN
IN THE SILVER MARKET

PROLOGUE

MEN OF ALL RACES have always sought for a convincing explanation of their own astonishing excellence and they have frequently found what they were looking for.

Thus, the Scottish historian Buckle established his fame by the discovery that civilisation was all due to climate. In an exhaustive survey of the climates of the world, he was able to range them in their order of merit. Hot, wet climates produced monstrous civilisations; hot, dry ones produced no civilisation at all, or if they did, the culture withered away. Extremely cold climates produced cultures of a low, huddling, grubbing and contracted nature. The best climate of all was temperate, varied, moderately rainy and briskly cold in winter. It was to be found in a fairly wide area, but particularly in the northwest corner of Europe. It was well exemplified in the climate of the British Isles, but perhaps it was best seen at its most vigorous best in that part of the British Isles which lay to the north of the River Tweed. Buckle's theories were well received in northwest Europe but did not gain much currency among the Spaniards, the Italians, or the Indians, while the Chinese, as is their custom, made nonsense of the whole thing because they have every sort of climate in the world.

A later theory was that natural selection determined that certain races should go to the top of the evolutionary tree and that others, owing to their lack of those qualities which led to survival, fell behind and ultimately became absorbed by the lucky winner. This theory held the field for a considerable time in England, particularly during those decades when the English were the greatest power in the world. Nowadays, when it would appear that Nature has selected them to be a secondary one, the theory gains no acceptance at all.

A third theory is that mankind are all brothers, but that some of the brothers are, for the time being, endowed with greater qualities than less fortunate brothers, and this superiority runs through a whole race. This is due to the Will of God (if you believe in God) or alternatively to History (if you know enough history). It is the duty of the more fortunate races to take the less fortunate ones by the hand (or, if they are stubborn, by the neck) and lead them to higher things. Meantime the less fortunate races should do as they are told.

No theory has been more widely held by men of goodwill among the white races. It is probable that it would be held by everybody, if it had not been applied by the Germans, not to coloured people as it was so clearly intended to be, but to white people who were not Germans. When this happened the theory was seen to be absurd and even pernicious. However, it convinced a great number of Germans that they could not lose a war because there was, logically, nobody good enough to beat them. So far, two attempts to introduce a higher standard of civilisation to the white races have met with stubborn resistance on the part of the natives: but a third effort is by no means an impossibility. Among the stubborn natives, however, the theory is not in good odour.

The most modern theory of all has the merit of great simplicity. It dispenses with God and Nature and confines itself to history. It says that history, when properly understood convinces all unprejudiced men that they ought to be Russians. But all men are not Russians. This would be an insuperable barrier if it were not for the Russians themselves, who have no desire to confine their immense advantages to their own nation, but eagerly press them on whoever asks for them. Thus everybody can be happy, if they are only sensible. This thesis has gained such wide acceptance in Russia that the rest of the world can only account for its success by holding that the Russians are not allowed to think for themselves. No doubt they are not, but even if they were, there is no reason to believe that they would come to any other conclusion. The English, for instance, have been free for a long while, and the idea that most people would really like to be English is by no means alien to them.

* * * * *

All these theories are, of course, absurd, but they are swiftly being replaced by another which is the most absurd of all. This says that there is no one is silly but honest to that in which he says, "My country, and it is never wrong," which is insane.

None of this has anything to do with the love of one's country. To love the fields, or the hills, or the town in which you are born; to like your neighbours better than strangers; to have a quicker sympathy with the people who speak your own language than with those who do not; to love and admire those people among whom you have chosen to make your home are virtues. I do not know that any sensible man has ever disputed them. I do know that civilisation is unthinkable without them. They have been defended, for all time, in that dialogue in which Socrates faces his last moments on earth. Since the day it was written, mature men have read it and known that in their heart of hearts they cannot deny the truth of the arguments though they might, not being philosophers, jib at the hemlock.

This love is patriotism. It is unfortunate that the most memorable phrase about it has been totally misunderstood. Samuel Johnson said it was the last refuge of the scoundrel, but two things should be remembered by anyone who quotes him. First, he says nothing in criticism of patriotism. Secondly

Johnson was speaking of a political faction that he did not like. Those were the scoundrels and patriotism was their mask. He meant no more than an opponent of the late Stanley Baldwin might have meant if he had said that frankness was the last refuge of a political trickster. Johnson did not say that a patriot is a scoundrel, which is false; he said that some scoundrels may claim to be patriots, which is true.

Here rises a dilemma. It is one which troubles many people but particularly, I think, the American. In his dealings with the rest of the world he wishes to say that sometimes his country is right. He finds however, in practice, that he cannot say convincingly that his country is sometimes right, without maintaining the attitude that his country is never wrong. If he does not, then his representatives will tell him, quite rightly, that he will be considered a weakling, and whatever bargain he makes will be a bad one. He did not intend that his love for his country should be used as a poker chip, but he cannot help it. Very soon he finds that his patriotism has led him to do things and say things through his representatives that he as an individual would consider wrong and vicious. Wishing to show that his patriotism is not an ignorant belief that his country is better than others and must be obeyed, he finds himself asserting just that very proposition in order to achieve some minor aim.

Thus in his dealings with the world he feels frustrated or guilty. To make sure that his reasonable prejudices cannot be thought a selfish nationalism he puts his faith in organisations where his country sits round a table with others, so that his point of view may be fairly compared with others and modified, if it seems that it should be. He is dismayed to find that when nations sit round a table, it is not the best of them that set the level of the discussion, but the worst. He feels that he has set his foot on a long, downwards slide, at the bottom of which his patriotism will be indistinguishable from that of the worst jingo or most selfish imperialist's.

* * * * *

Now a virtue cannot become a vice, except in a facile paradox. But a virtue may decay. It may become cancered and monstrous. Thus in ordinary morals to be pure in mind is a virtue. When this purity decays, the pure person seeks out impurity to test his own virtue. But his virtue is no longer strong enough to resist temptation and vice takes its place.

The virtue of patriotism can also decay. It can become monstrous and its monstrous form is the inflated nationalism against which the patriot, as I have shown, is now struggling.

In the pages which follow I briefly illustrate the decay of the most powerful patriotism of recent times, that of the English. I choose the English because their patriotism forms a part of the patriotism of every English-speaking person and of those who have been under English rule. I shall show, from my own experience, how it made people absurd.

HOW I WAS INITIATED INTO THE BEST TRIBE

BREATHES THERE A MAN (it has been asked) with soul so dead who never to himself hath said This is my own, my native land? I cannot answer the question but I find it flattering. If the principle behind it is true, I have a soul which so far from being dead is three times livelier than most other people's, for I have no less than three native lands which, provided I pay my taxes, I can call my own.

My ancestors on my mother's side were brigands who infested a range of hills overlooking the Lake of Killarney, called Macgillicuddy's Reeks. Two things are known to have run in their blood—a tendency to end up on the gallows and an itch to harry the English. I have managed to eradicate the first.

My ancestors on my father's side are Nayars of Malabar, a tropical stretch of country in the South of India. In the days when Malabar was ruled by a king, they performed the rite of cutting him up with scimitars at the end of a stated period of years. After this they chose another ruler. In due course he in his turn was ceremonially cut up by my ancestors, who chose another, and so on. They had no other democratic traits. They are to this day rigidly conscious of their class and strict in the observance of untouchability. They live by growing coconuts and grinding the faces of the poor, if by this it is understood that the operation takes place at the ritual distance of twenty feet from any member of my family. There has been some move towards more liberal ideas among them. But since by custom and by law women, and not men, are the heads of the family, this has made little progress.

My father, having run away from his family and come to England, married my mother. He was cut off with a rupee. One day, while my mother was discussing this difficulty with him she looked out of a window and seeing a baby said: "I know what we shall do. We shall have a son." My father to treat them as my masters. As an Englishman I was able to treat both the Irish and the Indians as my inferiors so long as I was careful to speak of them to their faces as my equals. This formula was the basis of an astonishing organisation called the British Empire and remained so until the formula was finally understood by the subject races, when the British Empire somewhat hurriedly became the Commonwealth. Since, however, it did not become a Commonwealth until the English had no wealth to share, the master race has been able to look back on the process without loss of self-esteem. Thus, even in the long view, my father's faith in my mother's sagacity was right. She brought me up as the member of a race that takes pride in itself, both for having an Empire and for not having one any longer: and a pride as broadly based as that is impossible to subdue.

There soon appeared, however, some temporary obstacles to my sharing it. These were instructive.

* * * * *

My childhood was passed during the first world war. At first I was made much of by the English and I was even given pennies by old gentlemen in the street. This was because some Indians on the Western Front were cutting the throats of Germans with a specially shaped knife called a *kukri*. This not only stirred the blood of all patriots but it also saved ammunition, the supply of which was a considerable problem at the time.

But towards the end of the war I was not so popular because I was mistaken for a Turk. This was liable to happen to anybody with a dark complexion. For a while I noticed unkind looks in the street and once or twice errand boys shouted after me. The Turks were reported to be cutting off the testicles of their English prisoners. Nobody charged me with doing this but because of my complexion I was considered to have at least proclivities in that direction. I endured, therefore, some hostility but this period did not last long: no longer, in fact, than the period between my fourth birthday and my reaching the age of four-and-a-half.

By the time I was six all was, in any case, forgotten and forgiven. Victory had been won and the Indians who had cut the throats of the Germans were to be seen in London, wearing the very knives with which they had done it, and I was popular again and once more old gentlemen gave me pennies in the street.

* * * * *

During this time my parents had tried to teach me to read but had met with no success. By the age of seven, however, I was found sitting on a hammock perusing Samuel Johnson's *Rasselas* with obvious enjoyment. From this I went on to *Tom Jones* and my parents considered it time to send me to school. Here I was set to read aloud to the class the adventures of Kim, my colouring adding drama to the recital. But I preferred *Tom Jones* and so did my little companions to whom I would tell the story serially, after school. This was the cause of the first real shadow to fall on my young life.

In view of my attachment to *Tom Jones* my schoolmistresses thought I was ready, and perhaps more than ready, for the more difficult works of Rudyard Kipling. During periods when other children were reading *Kim*, I was allowed to read more widely in the works of the master and his imitators. By this means I learned that besides the English, who were admirable, and the Indians who were also admirable but not to be relied on, there was a third sort of person. This third sort was never in the least admirable and was so persistently a traitor to all his acquaintances that it was a marvel that he could ever find anyone to trust him. This third sort of person was called a Eurasian.

I asked one of my schoolteachers what 'Eurasian' meant but she blushed deeply and passed me on to the Headmaster who said I would understand when I was older but that I must always remember that Jesus loved me. He then showed me a picture on his wall of the Founder of Christianity welcoming a great concourse of persons who pressed upon Him from every side each dressed in pointedly national costumes. I examined this attentively hoping to find a Eurasian who (as I knew from my reading) would be identifiable by his dirty ducks and battered topee. No figure answered to this description. This interview left me with the impression that Eurasians were such abandoned people that they found no place even in universal charity.

* * * * *

How I Was Initiated into the Best Tribe

I did not think of myself as one of these unfortunates at the time, and care was taken by my schoolteachers that I did not in the future. Their principles were liberal and so were their fees. They did not want my father to withdraw me. They saw to it that I was not caused an embarrassment which might have hurt them more than it might hurt me.

They therefore set about my education in this important matter with a will. I was rapidly made to understand that by great good fortune and a paternal Act of Parliament (but my mother's sagacity should have its due) I had been compulsorily registered within a short time of my having seen the light as having been born in England.

So I was an Englishman! Hurray for that, said my teachers. I remember that one of them in particular enlarged upon the many ways that I could have been born an Englishman, among them being born on board an English ship. This impressed me very much at the time and the impression remained with me. As I grew older it became entwined with the other curious knowledge that a boy acquires and for many years the thought of the Merchant Marine would conjure up for me pictures of Ocean

Greyhounds, flying the Red Duster, and loaded to the Plimsoll line with pregnant women of the most diverse nationalities, anxious to give their offspring the only start in life that really counted.

On all sides proud perspectives were opened to my view, some stretching back into geological time. As an Englishman I learned that I could feel peculiarly at home in the vast and—to foreigners—bewildering evolutionary process which is human history. In the first place evolution itself was discovered by an Englishman. From his researches it was established that Man originated in some sort of extinct ape. Slowly, in the passage of unthinkable aeons, his snout receded, his skull grew more domed, his teeth less sharp, his thumb more easily opposed to his fingers. There interposed a period when lesser breeds without the law ran riot on the earth, among the better of whom were the Greeks and the Romans. Then evolution took another step forward, approximately during the reign of Queen Elizabeth I, and my countrymen—or at the least my co-registrees—took their proper place in nature's hierarchy, which was in the van. But the process of evolution did not stop. It never stopped, even when there seemed no good reason why it need go on. Slowly, surely, the rest of the world was adopting English ways, buying English machinery, electing Parliaments on the English model and speaking what in due time would no doubt become less and less humourous varieties of English. I was a born part of this marvellous process and for a shilling at Somerset House I could get a copy of my birth certificate to prove it.

But this brought responsibilities with it and looking back I can see that these responsibilities weighed more on my instructors' consciences than they did on mine. I particularly worried all my teachers, from the mistresses of my infancy to the headmaster who sent me into the wider world, in the matter of telling the truth. Not that I was mendacious: but I so easily might have been, with my mixed ancestry. It had to be brought home to me that this would not do at all. An Englishman's word was his bond. It was especially important that I should learn this because I might very well spend parts of my life in, say, the Orient and it was there above all other places that the Englishman was respected as a man who told the truth. This great virtue of his did not count for so much in England. Indeed, there, one Englishman often told such black lies to another Englishman that the only way of getting at the truth was British Justice. This (no doubt from such exacting exercises) was the best in the world. But in dealing with foreigners, especially coloured races, an Englishman should always stick to the truth, although this was recognised to be no small part of the white man's burden.

I must also be courteous to foreigners, and more than courteous to foreigners who did not have my advantages. In all the twenty-four hours there was not one in which the sun did not shine on some part of the British Empire. In some areas it shone with great persistency, causing the inhabitants to be lackadaisical and summary in their habits. This should not make me scornful. Every person in the British Empire was a subject of the Crown. He had his rights, even if he were a naked and howling savage. The right which was most quoted to me (I cannot remember any others) was that if he were going to be hanged he could appeal to the Privy Council. This alone showed that he had a claim to my respect. Queen Alexandra was held up to me as an example and I learned how, at a dinner party, when some unfortunate Colonial guest drank out of the finger bowl, the Queen thoughtfully did the same. The passage of the years has not dimmed the glow of this anecdote for me. It does indeed show the Queen as the mirror of courtesy and when, in my 'teens, I saw her coffin pass me in the street, I took off my hat and bowed my head. She was a good woman and (as I then learned) Danish.

Thus by virtue of my birth certificate, my boyhood was spent, not in embittered isolation, but in the kindly company of people only too anxious to make me like themselves. If their well-meant instruction added up to the fact that my father was a congenital liar whose unfortunate habits I should tolerate and not rebuke, neither he nor I held it against them. He for his part silently paid my fees, while I, fortified by what I learned when I went to see my paternal grandmother, looked down upon the lot of them as my harmless, but dirty inferiors.

MY GRANDMOTHER
AND THE DIRTY
ENGLISH

MY GRANDMOTHER, LIKE MICHELANGELO, had *terribilità*. She had a driving will; she would not be balked and whatever she did was designed to strike the spectator with awe. She was also something of a stick. She rarely spoke to anyone who was not of her own social station and she received them formally: that is to say, with her breasts completely bare. Even in her time women were growing lax about this custom in Malabar. But my grandmother insisted on it. She thought that married women who wore blouses and pretty *saris* were Jezebels; in her view, a wife who dressed herself above her waist could only be aiming at adultery.

My Grandmother and the Dirty English

When I was twelve she demanded that I be brought and shown to her. I was incontinently taken half across the earth, from London to South beyond the town of Calicut. My mother came with me.

The last part of the journey was made by dugout canoe (there being no railways and no good roads near our family estate) and in this we were poled on a moonlit night up the Ponnani River. The river was lined with palm trees and crocodiles.

My mother taking fright at these beasts, I sang to keep them away from the boat. I sang a song I had been taught at school called "Drake's Drum." This had been written in the reign of Queen Victoria and told how, if the Spaniards should embark on the unlikely project of attacking nineteenth century England, Drake would come back to life and drum them up the Channel "as he drummed them long ago." I had been taught many songs of similar sentiments but this was the noisiest. I sang it with a will because my young heart (especially in such very foreign parts) glowed with the sentiment. The crocodiles yawned and, like the Spaniards in the Victorian age, showed no signs of attacking.

This singing marked a stage in my life. Shortly afterwards I lost my innocence. My grandmother took me in hand and I never thought the English were perfect again.

When our boat journey was done, servants with flaming torches led us along narrow paths between tall trees, and finally conducted us to a house. This house was large and smelt of paint. It was (my father said) not my ancestral roof.

* * * * *

When my grandmother had heard that my mother intended to make the visit as well as myself, she had given orders for a special house to be put in repair for my mother's accommodation. It was on the furthest confines of the family property. This was her solution of a difficult problem. My mother was ritually unclean, and therefore whenever she entered my family house, she would defile it. The house would have to be purified and so would every caste Hindu in it. It followed logically that if my mother stayed in the house, it would be permanently in a state of defilement and permanently in a state of being ritually cleaned.

Since this ceremony involved drums and conch shells, my mother's visit foreshadowed a prolonged uproar. All this was avoided by my grandmother's decision to put her up in a separate building.

I cannot say that my grandmother was ever rude to my mother. She never referred to her by name but always as 'the Englishwoman.' This was not necessarily an insulting expression, but my mother had Irish blood and what with this, and the house, and some other pin-pricks, her temper rose. She ordered a quantity of medical stores from Calicut, and when they arrived she set up a free dispensary on the verandah, to which the peasants flocked. It was an admirably devised answer. My grandmother had shut the door in my mother's face: she now had the galling experience of seeing my mother industriously cleaning up the doorstep. As my mother well knew, each drop of iodine that she dispensed stung not only the grateful patient, but also my grandmother's conscience.

My grandmother brooded on this for a while and then sent my mother a bag of golden sovereigns. My mother, taking this to be a bribe at the worst, or at the best, a tip, sent it back. But she was wrong.

It was a peace offering. It was sent again next day, accompanied by the family goldsmith who sat, slept and ate on the verandah for one week while he made the sovereigns (with tweezers and a charcoal fire) into a great gold collar which my mother still, on occasions, wears.

When, fourteen years before my trip, my father had written from England to say that he was getting married to a white woman, my grandmother had been far from giving the union her blessing. But it would be wrong to say that she had objected to it. If an American boy of twenty-two wrote home from foreign parts to say that he had taken to cannibalism, his parents would not object. They would be so revolted that a mere objection would never meet the case. So with my grandmother.

She had never met the English but she knew all about them. She knew they were tall, fair, given to strong drink, good soldiers and that they had conquered her native country. She also knew that they were incurably dirty in their personal habits. She respected them but wished they would keep their distance. It was very much the way that a Roman matron looked upon the Goths.

My eldest uncle had been to England for two years and he spoke up for the English. He said that while the Hindus were undoubtedly the most civilised race on earth and had been civilised a thousand years before the English, nevertheless, the English were now the masters of the Hindus. My grandmother's reply to this was that the English were masters of the Hindus only because 'nobody would listen to *us.*' By this she meant that our family along with others of the same caste had strongly objected to Vasco da Gama being allowed to land in Calicut. They had, in fact, done their best to get him and his sailors massacred. But the country was not behind them and he escaped. Everything, my grandmother argued (and not without some reason) had started with that.

But her chief complaint was that the English were so dirty, and this was rather a poser for my uncle. When my grandmother asked if, like decent people, they took a minimum of two baths a day, my uncle, who could not lie to his mother without committing a disgraceful sin, said that, well, no: but a few took one bath and the habit was spreading. He could go no further than that. But he added that my grandmother should remember that England had a cold climate. This she loyally did, and when she discussed the matter with me, she was able to treat the matter lightly, as one does the disgusting but rational liking of the Eskimos for eating blubber.

As for the question of eating, she did not have the expected prejudices. She did not think it strange that the English ate ham and beef. The outcaste hill-tribes (called *Todas*) who made the family straw mats and cleaned the latrines, ate anything. She was not disturbed either, about their religion, because my uncle assured her that they had practically none. Their manners, however, she abominated. If she did not mind them eating meat, she considered their way of eating it beyond the pale of decent society. In my family home, each person eats his meal separately, preferably in a secluded corner. The thought that English people could sit opposite each other and watch each other thrust food into their mouths, masticate, and swallow it, made her wonder if there was anything that human beings would not do, when left to their own devices.

She was not surprised to hear, after this, that in England a woman could have more than one husband, particularly (and this was the crowning paradox) if she had been a widow. To the day of her death my grandmother could never understand how people could call themselves civilised and yet allow widows to marry again. For her the very foundation-stone of society was that a child should have one father, and obey him. Nobody ever dared her wrath sufficiently to explain the position of women in English society. She was intensely proud of the standards of her house and she permitted no lewd talk to define them—certainly never in her presence.

With this background, then, my grandmother's peace offering of a bag of sovereigns was a considerable victory for my mother, particularly since the gold collar which the goldsmith had been told to make from them was the characteristic jewellery of a Malabar bride.

The way was now open for me. I could go and see her. I had waited about three weeks.

* * * * *

I had many meetings with her. I used to visit her in considerable state. The distance from our home—the isolation wing, so to speak—to the main family mansion was too far for walking in the Malabar sun. I used to go by palanquin. It was a hammock of red cloth with rather worn embroidery of gold thread, and it was swung on a black pole which had silver ornaments at either end. Four virtually naked men, two in front and two behind, carried the palanquin at a swift trot. There was considerable art in this. If the four men trotted just as they pleased, the hammock would swing in a growing arc until it tipped the passenger out on to the road. To prevent this, the men trotted in a complicated system that I never really understood: watching them and trying to trace it out was as difficult as trying to determine the order in which a horse puts its hoofs down. They kept their rhythm by chanting. I used to fall asleep on the way, listening to them. It must have presented an interesting spectacle—a red palanquin, the sweating men, and a sleeping schoolboy wearing an English blazer with its pocket sewn with a badge gained by infantile prowess at some sport that I do not now remember.

My Grandmother and the Dirty English

The family house was vast and cool and in my view, unfurnished. But to my grandmother's eye it was very elegant. There was nothing but the floor to sit on. She disliked chairs and thought them vulgar. What use were they, except for ostentation? She approved of beds but insisted that the mattress be made of taut string—nothing else was considered clean. She also had a taste for handsome brass-bound boxes. So beds, boxes and oil-lamps were the sole furniture of the innumerable rooms of the house. There were no tables and no table-cloths. In my grandmother's house, if anybody dared eat in any fashion but off a fresh plantain-leaf, his next meal would have been served in the kitchen, where the servants were allowed to eat without cere-mony.

My grandmother usually received me sitting by her favourite box in her boudoir. She made an un-forgettable picture. She had great black eyes, a shock of white hair and lips as lush and curved as a girl of eighteen. The skin of her bosom, bare as I have said, was quite smooth. I used to sit on the floor in front of her in my school blazer and since my father had never taught me Malayalam, (wishing me to be brought up like any other English schoolboy), we talked through one of my uncles.

The things my grandmother told me were a puzzle at the time. But I have come to understand them better. Much as she looked down on the English, I think that had she met some of them, had she overcome her well-bred fastidiousness and actually mixed with them, she would have found she and they had much in common. Her riding passion, like theirs, was racial pride. She believed—and this made her character—that she belonged to the cleverest family of the cleverest people on earth. According to Lord Russell, this was also the firm faith of Mrs. Beatrice Webb, who used to repeat it to herself in moments when, otherwise, she might have felt inferior, such as when she made her entry into a distinguished party. Though my grandmother never went to parties I'm sure that she, too, repeated the formula as a stiffener of her already formidable morale.

She felt that she was born of a superior race and she had all the marks of it. For instance, she deplored the plumbing of every other nation but her

own. She would often say to me, through my
uncle:

"Never take a bath in one of those contraptions
in which you sit in dirty water like a buffalo.
Always bathe in running water. If you have servants to pour it over you, that's best. But otherwise
you must stand under a tap or pour the water over
yourself. A really nice person does not even glance
at his own bath water much less sit in it." Here she
would laugh to herself, while my uncle translated;
not an unkind laugh, but a pitying one, as she
thought of the backwardness of the white man's
bathroom.

Another mark—and I have met it in many nations—was that she believed that English sexual
morals permitted and encouraged all sorts of abom-
inations from which a civilised person shrank. She
spoke to me with great freedom on this point: I was
after all at puberty. I could not always follow the
drift of her remarks, but I did gather that she felt
strongly on one point. Why, if the English wanted
their offspring to grow up decently and not lewdly,
did they omit to marry them off when they were
children? There was something sinister in the neg-

lect. A child should grow up knowing quite well that all that side of his life was settled according to the best available advice and in the best possible manner for his welfare. When he was eighteen or twenty the marriage would be consummated. Till then, he did not have to worry his head about women—or if he did worry, he knew he was morally slipping.

History, I have discovered, is on my grandmother's side. The great majority of civilised peoples have always agreed with her. Romance and love and such things were, in antiquity, things for slaves. Respectable families arranged their marriages as my grandmother arranged those of her offspring. To take a single example, my grandmother and Brutus would fully have understood each other. She felt hurt that she had not been consulted over my father's marriage: while among the many sidelights that we have on that honourable man who assassinated Julius Caesar is a letter in which he complains at being left out of the bargaining that went on during the betrothal of 'my dear little Attica,' who was nine years old.

But a grandson was a grandson, even although

her permission had not been sought to bring him into the world, and she set about being a mother as well as a grandmother to me. She knew that soon I would go back among the heathen to finish my education and she wanted me to go back knowing who and what I was. On one of my visits she gave me a small book in which was written all my duties and privileges as a member of my class. The book was written on dried palm-leaves, strung together with a cord between two covers of wood. It began with a prayer to God thanking Him for creating us—our caste, that is—so much superior in every respect to the great majority of other human beings.

My grandmother explained what followed several times and with much emphasis, for she wanted to imprint it on my memory. Our family belongs to the caste—or class—called Nayars. The Nayars of Malabar are as old as Indian history and therefore, it can be assumed, a good deal older. My grandmother told me that traditionally we had two obligations to society. We were warriors when there was fighting to do: and when there was not, we had the duty, on certain holy days, of carrying flowers to the temple.

I remember that I thought this very romantic at the time and could not understand why my grandmother took it so prosaically: to me, warriors, flowers and temples conjured up a picture of some Oriental Round Table. But my grandmother was right. Our caste is a commonplace: it exists everywhere. In England it is scattered all over the countryside. The men are what is called 'Army' and the women take not only flowers, but fruit to the temple on the occasion of the Harvest Festival. It is curious, and inexplicable, that the combination of these two activities, whether in the Shires or in the coconut groves of Malabar, produces the most ferocious snobs.

My grandmother explained to me that as a Nayar, I should always be very careful to keep my dignity when dealing with Brahmins: Brahmins are priests. The priests who have the cure of souls of my family are treated as domestic chaplains. Since their temples are on our property my grandmother had several 'livings,' so to speak at her disposal, this side of religious affairs always being left in the hands of the older women. Priests were therefore expected to make themselves agreeable, in return for which they were regularly fed. They were expected to mind their own business, which was to perform the weekly ceremonies and to direct their preaching at the lower orders, particularly the servants. The Anglican Settlement in England was much more elaborate but reduced to what it meant to the average priest-in-the-vestry, it came much to the same thing, and provides one more reason why I wish my grandmother had visited the country of my birth.

But my grandmother was quite ignorant of these striking resemblances and begged me when moving among the English to remember myself. "They will look up to you, as a Nayar, to set an example," she used to say. "They know that you have two thousand years of advantage over them and they will be willing to learn. Show them this book. They will be very interested. It was written when they still went about naked. And I will give you some trinkets which you can hand out as gifts: some amulets which we use and some things made of sandalwood, which is very rare in England so I am told, and much sought after. They will help you make friends. But remember, it is your *example* which will count more than anything."

She gave me all the things she promised and as she had foretold, they were much admired. Some of them, I believe, are still in my school museum. She also gave me her blessing, which was what I had been brought across the world to get.

I thought over her advice but I was in some confusion. My headmaster, wishing me good by and good-luck when I had set out on my trip had said much the same thing. "Let them see," he had said, "by your example that you have been trained in an *English* school. Wherever you go, it is for *you* to set the tone." He did not give me any sandal-wood, but I was very impressed. I was also very greatly impressed with what my grandmother had said.

In my dilemma I remembered that I had another grandmother. She had been born, as I have said, in Killarney, but had come to England to live—briefly enough, for she had died before I was born. I asked my mother about her. She told me many things but one stood out in my mind above all others.

"My mother," she said, "was never really happy

among the English. She longed to go back to Killarney. Sometimes when things had become unbearably tiresome, she would heave a long, deep sigh, shake her head and gently close her eyes."

I AM OFFERED
A MAGIC POTION

YOUNG AS I WAS, I felt that I understood my Irish grandmother. Life on our coconut plantations seemed much more desirable than the life which had dismayed her in England, and I began to feel that I would prefer not to return. While in England I was among people who constantly maintained they were the finest race on earth, here I was among people who thought the same thing but considered it so obvious that among themselves they never mentioned it. I found this more tranquil. Again, in England, I was taught to admire the working classes but on no account to copy their manners, their clothes or their accent; here the working classes stood at a distance of twenty feet from me. At that distance their manners were indiscernible, their accent inaudible and as for their clothes, to all intents and purposes save decency, they had none.

The Malabar climate was more relaxing than the English, but since I had been taught at school that a languid manner was the mark of a gentleman, I did not see that it could do me any harm: and I could not achieve greater nonchalance than when I was lying in a palanquin.

I enquired of my elders if it would be possible for me to live for the rest of my life on what were, after all, my ancestral estates and I was told that nothing could be simpler. I had merely to drink one full cup of the urine of a cow.

I was already aware of the virtues of a birth certificate. I was not so clear about the virtues of urine. But it was explained to me that my birth among the English had defiled me. According to the Hindus the cow has formidable spiritual powers and is capable of dealing with difficulties far greater than the one that I raised. To completely counteract the sad accident of being born in London a cow had merely to pass a little water. Once I had made its properties part of my own tissue I was well on the way to being an orthodox member of my caste.

From then on I should have to live more carefully; the cow could still rescue me from backsliding, but not so simply. Other crimes involved her other functions.

My uncles urged me to take this step. It was not only for the good of my soul: it was also for the good of my pocket. Without becoming an orthodox member of my ancestral religion it was difficult to see how I could lay claim to any of our ancestral coconuts: and these, yearly, brought in no inconsiderable sum of money.

I felt some hesitation and so I consulted my father.

He said:

"What is it that you object to? Is it drinking cow's urine that you don't like? Or becoming a Hindu?"

To which I replied that it was the cow and what went with it.

"You disappoint me," said my father. "If drinking the water of a cow is the most disgusting thing that you do in your life for the sake of money, you will be a singularly upright man. On the other hand, if you object to becoming a Hindu, then you are intelligent. I don't know exactly how many gods you will have to believe in but I think it is about three thousand. To have faith in three thousand gods may seem an easy thing at your age, but at my age I consider myself lucky that I can maintain my faith in one."

I therefore hesitated still further, until the monsoon broke with unprecedented violence, our house was flooded, and, making our way by boats over paths which we had walked when we arrived, we began our journey back to England and, for me, my school.

My headmaster was horrified at the idea that I had been offered a cup of excrement to make me a Hindu. He had a remedy of his own. He said that what I should do was to play games with balls of various sizes, with my whole mind and my whole heart and *that* would make me a fine, upstanding, young man acceptable to *English* society. I played games, having lost my opportunity to drink urine, but I approached one as reluctantly as I would have approached the other.

But I was in some perplexity over both advices. One group of my wellwishers thought that a cup of liquid could turn me into a Nayar with the duties of carrying flowers to the temple, bathing twice a day and putting twenty feet between myself and my caste inferiors: the other thought that physical exercise could turn me into an English gentleman. The trouble was how was I to choose? Each side maintained that it was the summit of creation. Each side maintained that the other was backward and dirty. My father said that when a person was faced with choosing between two paths, each of equal merit, he had observed that they usually chose the one that brought in the most money. Since I was now adolescent, I regarded this as base. I determined that I would remain independent of both groups, and that I would be myself.

This was a near approach to wisdom but unfortunately I took up the study of philosophy. Since I was much concerned with my own identity I was struck by a phrase of Descartes in which he said: "I think therefore I am," and I adopted this as a sort of motto. It seemed to be more individualistic than some such sentence as: "I have drunk cow's urine. I bathe twice a day, I do not eat in company, I avoid untouchables and therefore I am an orthodox Nayar with a stake in some coconut groves in the Southern extremity of India and I am considered a good boy": or "I am in the Second Eleven and may be in the First, and do not use diphthongs for my vowels and do not sneak and have no intention of subverting the King in Parliament and therefore I am a gentleman within the limits of my father's income and I am a good boy."

But here I soon saw I was wrong, for Descartes was not concerned with my problem at all. He was merely beginning an argument which did not end in proving that he was Descartes, come one come all against him; but ended by showing that he was part of a mechanical universe even more rigid and pre-determined than my grandmother.

Nevertheless, being by this time at a university, I persisted with my philosophical studies and grew to understand what very many of the philosophers were saying. Thus my mind fell into the uttermost confusion and I won several academic prizes. But in the course of my researches at the British Museum I chanced upon a book which described a national pride so pure and so quintessential that it revealed, at a blow, many aspects of my problem which I had ignored. Since the people concerned are not widely known, I ask permission of the reader to insert a short description of them.

* * * * *

The Jibaro Indians of Eastern Ecuador are described by outsiders as a primitive tribe. That is a bad description as I saw early in my reading. It does not help in understanding them: it actively obstructs. The Jibaros do not think of themselves as a tribe: they are a nation and, considering the elaborate nature of their daily lives, they cannot be expected to think of themselves as primitive. In fact their obstinate adherence to their own forms of correct behaviour is threatening to destroy them, if, by this time, it has not done so already.

Every member of the Jibaro nation is devoted to the national task of cutting off the organs of generation of their male enemies. Their enemies are everybody that can be reached in a brisk night's journey by foot outside the national boundaries. The trophies are collected, brought back and counted. The national mood is set by the size of the number. If it is large all right-thinking men and women rejoice in their national prowess and heartening ceremonies take place, in which the trophies and the blood connected with them play a large part. The actual chopping off is the privilege of the men: but they have the other sex wholly behind them. The women and the children who are old enough to walk do all the domestic chores and till the fields. They also organise the comforts and encouragements which are showered on the men before an expedition, as well as the lengthy national rejoicings when they return. If by ill-fortune or some temporary decay in the national character the trophies are sparse or—a disaster—if they have been collected by the enemy, the women take on their burden of the blame. They move about their daily tasks morosely, weighed down with feelings of shame and guilt which can only be removed by another and more successful expedition.

This soon takes place and all is well again. Long practice and something which is held to be part of the national character of a true Jibaro, makes the men singularly adept at the swift obtaining of trophies: and a little intensive training of the younger males brings this out in each generation.

They have no other education to confuse them. Their mothers, being like-minded and filled with the spirit of the community, assist in producing a uniform atmosphere of pride in the past achievements of the nation and determination to surpass them in the future.

No other talent is encouraged, or, in fact, permitted. Like most South American Indians they once had a rudimentary form of art. But everybody knows how war absorbs artists, and the Jibaros have reduced their creative urge to tying tassles on their trophies. Again, eating is a necessary business: but it need not be allowed to waste time which might be spent in killing. Jibaro meals are therefore simple and hasty and they are accompanied by shrill advice from the women to their husbands to get up and go about their business. The sexual act itself is performed with the desire to have a planned population, by which is meant that each family will be able to send its quota of strong young men each year when the call-up comes. Religion presents no difficulties: God is pleased with trophies and nothing else. The larger the offering, in all senses, the more He is pleased, since He fights on the side of the Jibaros. Like other nations at war, the Jibaros are relieved of all care about material wealth —it all goes into the war-chest.

They are a small nation, but gallant. Their population is falling in spite of the patriotic efforts of the women, and of the men (when they are on leave from the front). Although they are uniformly successful in warfare (there is at least no recorded or remembered defeat that was not amply revenged) the cost in life is often very high. The burden of expenditure on arms—poison arrows, spears, and knives—is back-breaking, and the poor diet, made necessary because time cannot be wasted in growing better food, produces an alarming degree of illness. The American observer who lived among them felt that it was entirely possible that the whole tribe would one day be destroyed. They are quite aware of this. But they feel they must follow their national destiny, come what may. So they tighten their belts—or they would if they wore any—and go off to war again, thirsty for the male organs of generation of the national enemy, and for glory.

The explanation of the conduct of these people did not surprise me very much. I could recognise the signs of their principal belief well before I had completed my reading. They were a superior nation. It was part of their religion. They were better, stronger, wiser and more civilised than their neighbours, being specially favoured by the celestial Ju-jube.

Unfortunately they could only remain worthy of this distinction if they could collect, each year, a sufficiently large pile of trophies to offer to the Ju-jube. If they did not, he would withdraw his support and they would fall from their position on the pinnacle of the human race.

Now, they were deceived. A collection of human members does not necessarily prove that a nation is pre-eminent. There are rival collections. America has a collection of gold: England—at least when I was studying the Jibaros—had a matchless collection of other people's landed property: Germany had guns: Italy, art treasures: Japan had soldiers of an unparalleled devotion. Slash as they might, the Jibaros would never equal, much less surpass these nations. Their thinking was wrong.

I could see this, sitting in the Reading Room of the British Museum. But a moment's reflection showed me that if I were sitting astride a fallen enemy in Eastern Ecuador, with the encouraging shouts of my Jibaro comrades ringing in my ears, I would not see it.

As a philosopher I expressed this in logical terms: from any set of premises one could make a number of deductions, often of vast extent. These would be true if the premises were true, false if (as in the case of the Jibaros) they were false.

As a philosopher, this satisfied me. But as a young man with a problem of my own I determined to take a steady look at the English.

I returned my books to the Librarian, left the shelter of the Reading Room and moved out into the world.

I was at this time a dramatic critic and I had leisure in the day-time for my researches. I frequented the debates in the House of Commons, contrived to gain admission to the House of Lords, and I moved in such society as I could command with a dress-suit and a spare free ticket for the play and the opera. I week-ended in the country: I dined in clubs: I addressed meetings in the industrial north on any topic the secretaries required for the sake of studying the subsequent questions: and I never forgot the poor deluded Jibaros.

I found that the English were suffering under a delusion which would have been thought extraordinary, even in Eastern Ecuador.

A SHORT GUIDE
TO THE
ENGLISH OLIGARCHY

I BASED MY ENQUIRIES on a list of things of which I thought the English might well be proud. It was a formidable list. Of the three greatest influences on world history—The Romans, Christianity and the English—the English came third only in point of time. I therefore had a great wealth of achievement from which to choose. My selection ranged from Chaucer and Shakespeare to the steam engine and anaesthetics: from the spinning jenny to the Factory Acts; from Gibbon to Wilberforce. I discussed this list with the best informed people. This led to the point of departure for my discoveries, which I shall now summarise in a conveniently itemised form.

[53]

1. *Of what the English are most proud*. It was none of the items on my list. I was told that the thing which they held to be most typically English and their greatest contribution to the world was practical political liberty. I investigated this.

2. *Liberty*. Liberty as a political notion was not discovered by the English (they do not say it was). The claim to have discovered it is disputed but the strongest one is put forward by the French. Political liberty did not, however, become a practical thing until the Americans started shooting at the English in the American Revolution. They were not the first people to shoot at the English—it would have been most remarkable if they had been—but they were the first to do it from a decent respect for the opinions of mankind. Thus they linked their own shooting with French thinking. So much for history: it does not affect the English claim to have made liberty practical, which is perfectly just. The French thinkers drew their inspiration from English practice, which they much admired. They also admired the Americans, who refused to live under it. This is a paradox but not

illogical. As much as advanced Frenchmen admired the Engilsh system, they too showed no desire to live under it. Rousseau and Voltaire both visited England but left for France as soon as it was convenient. What was this system?

3. *The Oligarchy.* The principle on which the English founded their liberty was that it was unthinkable that every Englishman should share it. They sang, one and all, that Britons never never should be slaves, but that was as far as they were prepared to go in making general promises. Nobody would be a slave (nobody had been since the days of William the Conqueror) but as for the proposition that men were equal, this was a French tomfoolery, and the Englishman denied it. They built, instead, a class-conscious society. This was divided into two groups. The first consisted of a small number of families who between them shared all the seats in Parliament, all the Offices of the Crown, all the high posts in both the Universities, all the bishoprics, both archbishoprics, all other wealthy ecclesiastical positions, and all sinecures whatsoever. The second group consisted of everybody else.

This arrangement so amazed the Jew Disraeli when he, like myself, had studied it in detail, that he said that there was not one England but two. Nobody contradicted him. Of the two Englands, Disraeli, by titanic exertions, gained entry into the one that ruled. He even became Prime Minster (not by any means a job which every English gentleman would take). But so exclusive was the ruling class that although Disraeli was their pet and their Premier he felt so much an outsider that he referred to the English not by the word *we*, but *you*. ("You," he remarked,—for instance—"had an Englishman, Sir Walter Raleigh, who gave you the potato and who gave you tobacco. And what did you do with him? You cut off his head.")

The manner of operating of the oligarchy that its own Prime Minister addressed as 'you' is well-known in its broader features. The children of a limited number of families were given a limited education in a limited number of schools. They were trained to conform to the arbitrary habits of the oligarchy, down to such small details as the pronunciation of vowels and the number of buttons on their coats. They were also taught a manner and a deportment which could be recognised anywhere so that if a member of this class were deprived of every outward manifestation of his rank,—if, for instance, he were caught in his bath—he would still be seen instantly to be a gentleman and accorded the privileges due to him. As a caste system it far surpassed anything devised by the Indians. It even outreached the subtlety of the Chinese. The Manchus made everybody who was not a Manchu wear a pigtail. But pigtails could be (and were) cut off. Nothing could remove the marks of an Englishman of the ruling class.

Once marked, he was taught to be loyal to others so marked. These others, in turn, helped him by giving him one of a great number of positions in society to which money payments or money advantages were attached: and since the public's pocket is the deepest of any, most of these positions were connected with the government of the country and, later, the Empire.

He was not supposed to show any outstanding aptitude for these posts: he was not expected to have any merit. But he was definitely expected to avoid making mistakes. If he made them, he would be at first loyally protected by other members of his class. If he went on making them he would be honourably retired. If, by chance, and in spite of his careful education, he showed genius, he would be praised, but not liked.

The system avoided sharp changes in policy: it avoided faction or at least the worst bitterness of factions. It made for temperance and level-headedness in the conduct of affairs; since each man only barely knew his job, few were seized by new and disturbing ideas. Further, since most men could be sure of being allowed to make money in an honest way without interference from outsiders, it discouraged competition. It had every argument in its favour including that of many successes which did not belong to it.

4. *The Cads.* It did not properly get under way until the Glorious Revolution. Before that the two successful periods of English history had been that of the Elizabethans—who were no more ruled by gentlemen than they were by a lady—and the Protectorate of Cromwell, who had come to power precisely by overthrowing the King's attempt at

the creation of a governing class. The new system of rule by oligarchy led off with some notable achievements but by the end of the eighteenth century it had lost America. It began the nineteenth century by just defeating Napoleon at that 'very near thing' as Wellington described Waterloo. But it was Wellington whose windows were stoned by a crowd furious at its shortcomings, and it was Wellington who finally acquiesced in the first inroads on its monopoly of power. The system was saved from ruin by the invention and industry of the class below it. England led the world in the Victorian era. But it was not a triumph of the English gentleman. It was a triumph of the English cad who amassed more money, by means of a greater inventiveness, than the world had ever seen before. Fortunately the cad's dearest ambition was to be a gentleman, so, when the tin-smith and the iron-master had bought some land and got his son in the right school, the system went on as before. As a result of this solidarity, by the beginning of the twentieth century (which was the last time an English gentleman could honestly pay his way) the oligarchy of England were the admiration of

admired the Navy and explained their preference by saying that they were a seafaring people. So far as the oligarchy was concerned this was a plain untruth. Like any other sensible landsmen the country gentlemen of England avoided going on the sea whenever they could, and when they could not they were as sick and miserable (to judge from their diaries) as any Tartar. But as a race the English fought at sea with a thirst for glory that they never had on land and although they were not cowards in either element, they took a beating on land as a very ordinary affair, while a defeat at sea they looked upon as a shameful disaster. Yet they produced generals who were quite as good as their admirals and sometimes much better. Marlborough, Clive, Wellington were as competent soldiers as the world has ever seen. But it is curious that Wellington so shared the general prejudice against soldiers that he despised his own troops and never lost an opportunity of telling them so. When reviewing them, as everyone knows, he remarked "I don't know if they will frighten the enemy, but by God they frighten me."

No explanation has ever been offered for this

dislike of the English oligarchy for land wars. A possible reason is that land wars have to be fought abroad among foreigners and foreigners were considered a distasteful lot. Earl Baldwin, while presiding over Cabinet meetings was accustomed to go to sleep when foreign affairs were mentioned, saying: "When you're finished, wake me up."

But the unwashed French and gluttonous Germans and some allied foreigners had been altering the art of war. Frederick William of Prussia had shown how a whole nation can be placed on a war footing and kept there. Napoleon, adroitly profiting by the fervour raised in the French by the Revolution, had shown how the whole young manhood of a nation could be called upon to do the fighting. When the next large war broke out and the English joined in, their small force of professional soldiers was instantly overwhelmed. When the Germans described the British Expeditionary Force as a contemptible little army, their manners were bad but their military judgement was sound. The English then raised an army that was neither little nor contemptible and which was in the end victorious. But it was not an army of gentlemen nor even gentlemen's dependents. It was an army of conscripts.

In the first months of that war the English at home were greatly heartened by stories from the front that told how Englishmen were throwing grenades at the enemy with the verve (and the overarm motion) of a cricketer bowling at a wicket; and how the boys had gone over the top kicking a football. But lists of the dead and the mutilated that stopped men's hearts soon brought home the fact that the Germans were playing neither cricket nor football but a much more deadly game. The English had not been foolish. They had been cruelly disappointed. The education, the stance, the principles and the nonchalance of the English oligarchy were held to be the summit of what a man could be. No Englishman aspired to anything better and what was good enough for the Englishman might well be held to be good enough to beat the foreigner. But it was not.

In the resulting slaughter of its young men the English oligarchy took a defeat, moral and physical, from which it never recovered. The cads were called in to save the day and when they did not come in sufficient numbers, they were dragooned. The war over, these same citizens wanted to know what they had been fighting for. There was some considerable delay and then, at last, the oligarchy was able to answer that they had been fighting for democracy, personified, if somewhat equivocally, by the first low-class Prime Minister of England, the envelope-addresser Ramsay Macdonald.

The oligarchs were finished. They knew this themselves quite well. They maintained a political party to act as their executors but otherwise they slowly retired from the centre of the stage of history, allowing their functions, their privileges and their fortunes to fade one by one, maintaining all the while the greatest amiability, until, like the Cheshire cat, nothing was visible of them but a large grin, and that only at election time.

6. *An Echo from Ecuador.* But in a free country you cannot fool all of the people all of the time. Some of them will have a talent for fooling themselves and they will insist on exercising it.

No sooner had the English oligarchy withdrawn than there began, up and down England, an intensive propaganda in favour of the principles which it had abandoned. The manners, customs and beliefs of the English gentleman became an object of almost religious study by authors, journalists, schoolmasters, parents and young people. The enthusiasm swept all classes of English society, save that of the oligarchy itself, which had no time for it, the best of its members having found jobs, the others having taken to drink or Kenya.

The schoolmasters, in particular, were most energetic. In the peace which followed the war they turned out a generation of gallant young officers whose men would have followed them with dog-like devotion, if only there had been some fighting. In the financial slump of the thirties they turned out a generation of splendid gentlemen who were ready to be as good as their word and pay every man his due, if only they could find a tradesman sufficiently foolish to give them some credit. Meanwhile the public which read books and newspapers were convinced that every Englishman was born frank, truthful, guileless, open-handed, loyal and imperturbable, virtues which called for a private income of not less than five thousand pounds a year. The illusion that nothing had changed was universal, or nearly so.

Two sections of the community were however cut off from their fellows by the nature of their profession—coal-miners and the Royal Family. The coal-miners struck work on reasonable grounds and were met with such hostility from that part of the community that was living in its dreams in the age of the young Victoria, that they became embittered and have remained embittered down to this day. The King, superficially and carelessly educated in his boyhood, had escaped the schoolmasters; not being given to reading in an extensive way, he attempted to show in his manner of living that the times had changed since those of his grandfather. He was driven from the throne.

Slightly before this, the politicians who had been put into parliament merely as executors for the deceased oligarchy, had found themselves kept in power by an enthusiastic electorate which bluntly refused to be governed by Ramsay MacDonald unless he promised to associate with gentlemen. Mr. MacDonald did his best in this direction by forming a Coalition government, but it was too much for him. He retired, exhibiting symptoms of logomania, and the world was presented with the spectacle of its leading power being governed by a class which no longer existed, represented by men who resolutely refused to do anything whatsoever, and who were regarded as the saviours of their country.

The extraordinary delusion of the English had reached its climax, but not its end. The government had been elected on the slogan "Safety First." What came second nobody knew at the time, and in the event, nobody ever did find out. While a record number of people whom the electors could look upon as thorough gentlemen sat in the House of Commons, some two million workmen without jobs paraded the streets.

Englishmen who were convinced that no more perfect system of government than the English one had been invented since the Holy Ghost dictated Leviticus and Deuteronomy, accused the unemployed of not wanting to work. The unemployed might have replied that in that case they were only showing their gentlemanly instincts: but they were not aware that in all the best schools in England at that time the children were being taught that the finest qualities of the English character could only be displayed if one had what was called 'independent means.'

Safety having been put first and the armed forces partially disbanded (on the oligarchic principle of disliking the soldier), the government found little else to do and the country had no suggestions.

The increasing poverty of the country was blamed onto the failure of American markets: the unemployed were bought off (in the manner of the Roman Empire at its wealthiest) by doles. The Prime Minister had so little to talk about that he took to recommending good books on the English countryside. He retired, was loaded with honours, and was succeeded by another who, if less bucolic, was no less gentlemanly. The final ruin was very near.

7. *The Awakening*. One of the taunts from which the ex-envelope-addresser MacDonald suffered was that he was over-fond of going abroad to talk with foreigners. It was deemed that no true oligarch would have felt the necessity for travel and

the Prime Oligarch, above all, should stay at home. This may have been arrogant but it may also have been true.

For we have now reached the Premiership of Neville Chamberlain. Had this particular Prime Minister stayed at home, the attitude of the English towards world affairs would have been interpreted by all foreigners, including the Germans, as being dictated by Machiavellian guile, and as a prelude to unexampled perfidy. Unfortunately he went in person to Godesburg and Munich and the diplomats of Europe, peering into his decorous face, came to the conclusion that he meant what he said. What he said, confronted with the German plan to enslave Europe, was, in substance, that he had no comment.

He was the epitome of nonchalance. He had visited the continent, treated the foreigners' knavish tricks with contempt and showed them that not only were the English not afraid: they did not even know what they were supposed to be afraid of. On his way back to England he thought of an apt quotation. Faced with economic collapse, Mr. Baldwin had quoted Mary Webb. Faced with Armageddon, his successor quoted Shakespeare. Following the quotation he made a short speech, "Go home," he said kindlily to the ordinary people who had gathered in the streets, "and sleep quietly in your beds." They went, after a rousing cheer. The country thought the whole thing was magnificent: and it was not war.

But, of course, it was. Among the theories evolved by the more thoughtful people of pre-war England for dealing with the unemployed was that in a modern state it was a perfectly sound thing to set unemployed people to work to dig unnecessary holes in the ground and then pay them to fill them in again. This policy did not win wide support in England (it was exported to America), but many people felt it should be tried. In the end the holes were dug, but not by the unemployed. They were dug by busy Germans throwing high explosive at England's cities.

Even now, seven years after the end of the war, all these holes are not filled in. The English are too poor: and of all the luxuries with which they have had to part, the one they most regretted to see go was the illusion that they were a nation ruled by gentlemen of leisure, and that these gentlemen of leisure ruled by God's command.

A discerning and intelligent Englishman once said to me during the last war, "When I saw St. Paul's Cathedral outlined against the huge fire which broke out among the publishers' warehouses in Paternoster Row, I knew, deep down inside me, that the Old Order was finished." Thus for an Englishman (and there were many like him) the sight of a church into which the Oligarchs rarely went, surrounded by burning books which the Oligarchs never read, was the final proof that the war had finished a social system, which did not exist.

8. *The Political Theory of the Cosy Corner.* The general political theory of a civil oligarchy can be found in the 'Politics' of Aristotle: its extensions to religious affairs is outlined in the 'Institutes' of Calvin; and a useful critique of this is provided by Richard Hooker. The political theory of oligarchy as practised by the English can be stated in more simple terms.

I must first remove some misapprehensions. It

is not as many people think, a mental disease of the British, nor is it their way of showing Original Sin. It is not like a tattoo mark, something wilfully disfiguring which charitable people try to ignore. It is as natural to an Englishman as his teeth: and although in England's old age he may be forced to fit himself with other arrangements, they will never be for him like his own.

I live on what is nowadays called the Italian Riviera: that is to say, I live on a coast which the Greeks, the Romans, the Italians, the Spaniards, the Germans, the Swiss, the Swedes, and recently the Americans have chosen as a place of delectable beauty and exquisite climate: a place where life can be led easily and pleasantly. The visiting Englishman describes it as pretty, warmish and uncomfortable. I speak from my own experience.

What does the visiting Englishman miss? He misses being cosy. This is an Englishman's passion. Psychologists, mostly foreign, have described it as an *inter-uterine complex*, a desire, that is, to return to the womb. Some madmen among the English may have wished for such a thing, but there is no trace of insanity among the rest. If it is insisted that a desire for cosy corners is a complex, then the womb that the middle-class Englishman wishes to return to would have a coal-fire, a rug, a cat, a dog, a radio broadcasting the nine o'clock news, and well-curtained windows giving on to a small strip of garden. I think it less of a strain on the imagination simply to say that the Englishman wishes to be snug and safe in his own home.

The essence of snugness is security. There is a fire to protect one from being cold, company (the cat, the dog and perhaps a wife) to protect one against boredom, heavy furnishings to guard one from draughts, the newspaper and the radio to remind one deliciously of the perils of life outside the nest. But above all, the front door is locked against intruders. Here we find the seed from which the spreading tree of the English oligarchic system has grown.

The thing which the Englishman wishes most to be protected from is the company of other Englishmen—not from all of them, but from most of them. He finds their manners coarse, their conversation tedious, and their tastes embarrassing. But he is not a misanthrope. There is always a small group of his fellow countrymen whose manners he finds acceptable, whose conversation is absorbing and whose tastes are his own. He wishes to associate with these and these alone. He would found a monastery with them if he believed in God. Instead he founds a club. A club is the acme of cosiness and the acme of clubs was the House of Commons which, in the hey-day of the English Oligarchy was described by the English themselves as the best club in the world.

It has often been remarked that England taught the world the system of Parliamentary government, but that with the foreigners a Parliament soon becomes a very odd affair. This is because no country, when adopting the Parliamentary system, adopted the most essential feature of its cosiness which was the 'rotten' borough. A 'rotten' borough was a place which sent a representative to the House of Commons by means of the votes of a small number of persons who could be bribed or bullied into voting for a certain number of families.

Most of these families also had the right to appoint priests to what were, with British directness called 'livings.'

By these means a gentleman of substance and

good family could make tolerably sure that neither the laws of man, nor those of God, would ever face him with an unpleasant surprise.

As we saw at the beginning, the essence of this system was that it could not be shared by everybody. However, its virtues were mystically supposed to spread throughout the whole national body, so that the definition of any good Englishman was that he held that the majority of his fellow countrymen were not fit company for himself, his wife, and his family. This is a paradox which defies any further logical analysis.

I shall conclude by drawing attention to one consequence. Since oligarchs die and do not always leave a fortune to their children, some provision had to be made for recouping the financial position of the ruling class. This was done by marriage, at a price, with women of the lower orders. The fathers of suitable women had therefore to exert themselves to earn money, and save it when they had done so. They were also well advised to have some smattering of the tastes of their betters, since, as pure Yahoos, they would be too offensive to negotiate the necessary marriage arrangements. Among the middle-classes therefore, industry, thrift and education became paramount aims.

I shall have occasion to refer to these when I tell, subsequently, of a Maharajah, a Knight, and a Fakir.

I AM PUT INTO
THE WRONG HERD

HAVING COMPLETED MY STUDIES OF THE ENGLISH I
went to my second country which is Ireland. Calling
upon the Government on some professional duties,
I was shown to a simple office on the glass door of
which was written:

AN TOESACH

An obliging civil servant translated this for me
as, 'The Herder of the Herders.'

Inside the office I was courteously received by
a tall man of impressive appearance and engaging
manners. This was Mr. Eamon De Valera.

In the course of an extensive conversation I explained to Mr. De Valera that I was visiting what I

[77]

held to be one of my ancestral countries, among the others being England.

Mr. De Valera, thereupon told me with much vivid detail how he had escaped from a prison in in which the English had put him.

With the Herder's good wishes (for such was the Prime Minister's title) I toured Ireland by motor-car, in the company and under the instruction of the Irish.

On the corners of a great number of roads there were crosses of white marble, bearing a name, a date and the inscription:

A MARTYR TO BRITISH IMPERIALISM

Since the motor-car was always brought to a halt in front of these crosses, and since I was always invited to dismount to read the (unvarying) inscription and to hear the story, it was borne upon me in the course of some 1000 miles and 200 crosses that my researches among the English had,—as so often happens—left their mark upon me. A cattle farmer, closely associated with bulls and cows (for instance) often acquires a bovine manner.

I *Am Put into the Wrong Herd*

Leaving Ireland, I determined it was high time to visit my third country, as a corrective. In 1939 I went to India.

THE HAPPY LAND

I WAS FORTUNATE in my Indian friends and not very long after my arrival in my third native land, I was invited to stay for a while in a Princely state and to write, if I chose, a book about it. My friends urged me to accept for, they said, this State had been left alone by the English owing to the extreme loyalty of the people to their Ruler, for whose independence they had fought ferociously until the day that they discovered that he had, some time before, already signed a treaty of capitulation in return for a large cash payment.

But the English had decided by this time to conquer all India and could not spare troops for the subjection of this obdurate people. They therefore signed another treaty with the ruler who had succeeded (with violence) the traitor, which left the land in peace, in consideration of the return of the cash payment. An English Resident had been sent for the sake of form. But he was, and remained till recent times, under strict instructions to do nothing whatever but reside. This task he found easy for the climate was equable and the shooting among the finest in the world.

The present Ruler was benevolent. He had put an end to the various attempts to collect taxes which had been made by his predecessors and which had always failed. Early in the nineteenth century a land-tax had been imposed, at which the inhabitants allowed all fields within two miles of the Palace to go untilled. The jungle made rapid advances and a tiger having surprised His Highness as he was making to his private closet (which was situated in a rose garden) the tax was repealed. An income tax was next levied but the returns showed that nobody had any income. A tax on tobacco caused everyone to give up chewing it. By these tactics the inhabitants had always beaten the best financial brains that were brought against them. When, however, a tax was placed on food, they changed their tactics and beat the tax collectors.

The present Ruler had abolished all major taxes and made, instead, the sale of ice-cream a State monopoly. The inhabitants had a great passion for this delicacy, and it was otherwise unobtainable. They therefore paid willingly. The revenue was small and did not permit any progress such as education, the building of railways, the opening of mines, the introduction of factories, the subsidising of newspapers, the erection of radio transmitters or the payment of an efficient police force. Thus His Highness was loved to the point of devotion by his happy subjects, whom, since I was in search of the real India, I was urged to visit.

* * * * *

I found that the State was as beautiful as its sons were loyal. The palace was low and white. It was surrounded by gold mohur trees. The guest house was large and cool. It was surrounded by gardens modelled, except for the notices, on the Green Park, Piccadilly. The town, which lay some distance away, was pink. It had a profusion of minarets and a wall. The wall was pierced with pointed gateways, called Thursday Gate, the Friday Gate and so forth. But within the gates it was always Sunday afternoon.

His Highness received me kindly, smoking a hookah, and talked of polo. Knowing nothing of this sport, I turned the conversation to literature, thus producing a draw. I was dismissed after half an hour with a pressing invitation to shoot a tiger and visit the ice-cream factory. In the ante-chamber, on being questioned by the courtiers I said that I was astonished by His Highness' open and democratic manner and amazed at the range of his conversation.

An assistant chamberlain was deputed to show me all that I needed for the purposes of my book and an automobile was put, through him, at my disposal.

The Chamberlain was extremely fat and amusing. With the aid of a map he planned an exhaustive tour of inspection for the following weeks. The start of this was delayed from day to day for reasons which were not explained to me. The Chamberlain visited me each morning full of apolo-

gies and scandalous stories. One evening he directed
my attention in time to a snake curled up on a chair
on which I was about to sit, by this breaking down
all reserve between us. I never sat on a snake again
in India which makes me think that the Chamberlain was not as surprised to find a snake on my
chair, as it appeared, nor the snake as dangerous.

However that may be the Chamberlain seized
the opportunity to suggest an arrangement which
he said had been much in his mind since the
weather had turned surly. He said:

"Instead of driving around the State in all this
heat, which will be bad for you, coming from England, why don't you stay in this beautiful cool guest
house and I will bring you all the information you
can use. Also some that you can't, to relax your
mind after the day's work." He then shifted the
quid of tobacco in his enormous left cheek to his
right, spat in a silver plated spittoon and went on,
"Meanwhile I shall turn that little knob affair by
the speedometer of the car and make it register the
exact number of miles which you are supposed to
have travelled."

I asked: "Will that be necessary?"

He replied that it would.

I said, "But I can't see why."

He answered: "Well, if I don't do that I cannot draw the petrol for the run."

"No," I agreed, "but then we won't have any use for the petrol."

"Oh, but *I* shall," he said. "I shall sell it." He folded his hands across his belly, closed his eyes, and chewed upon his tobacco, taking my consent for granted and feeling at peace with the world.

I said that it would not do. It was H.H.'s petrol so it was none of my business if his courtiers stole it. But I would have to make some trips, at least. I protested that I had a book to write.

He protested, in his turn, that he had a wife and six children.

I did not then and I do not now consider a book more important than a wife and one child, much less six (it would be monstrous if I did) so from principle, I agreed with his scheme.

He brought me useful information and the

speedometer registered praiseworthy industry. I began the book. The preface was to be spoken by a tiger. Since the ice-cream factory was near at hand, I visited that, and the petrol used being very small, my trip made almost no difference to the Chamberlain's wife or any of the six children. But my tiger had nothing to say about ice cream and on being pressed to do so, fell into a silence.

* * * * *

Since I was no longer writing a book I had more time to listen to my friend. I discovered other things about this happy land.

One of them was that my friend had been awarded a handsome salary for looking after His Highness' guests. For some years this had not been paid and would not be paid in the future unless the inhabitants' appetite for ice-cream increased beyond all reasonable expectations. He had therefore resorted to the system I have described, which worked very well since the cost of the petrol came out of the Ruler's private purse. When I asked whether it would not be simpler for the Ruler to pay the salary, I was told, with some emphasis, that it would not.

Again, I learned that when the inadequate police force which was grossly underpaid, arrested a criminal and got him convicted, the criminal was handed over to the Governor of the local jail, who was not paid at all. Here the criminal rotted until he paid the Governor a bribe, assessed according to the length of his sentence, when he was released on indefinite parole. Since the bribe was always very heavy, the criminal usually denounced his relatives for various imaginary crimes. They were then arrested, sent to the jail, and in these unpleasant circumstances the hat was passed round and the bribe paid. This had the result that should the criminal wish to return to his bad habits, his relatives acted as an unpaid but enthusiastic police force of their own accord.

I found objections to this system as well.

My friend answered me:

"You do not understand. This is a very small State and we all know each other's ways and we all think alike. So we all love our life and if we do not, we can always leave. We do not leave because we are loyal and we are loyal because we are happy. I have often wondered why we are so happy. I think it is because our State is so small."

All the statements in this book are true, but this is one of the most true. I did not see it at the time; however, I looked upon my stay there as a pleasant interval.

*   *   *   *   *

This interval was brought to an end when I received an invitation from a neighboring Prince to go and stay with him. This placed me in a pleasant difficulty, since I had not received my *congé* from my present host. I consulted my Chamberlain. He replied:

"I quite understand your difficulty. Leave it to me. We are quite used to it. You see, for two hundred years the ancestors of the Maharajah who has written to you used to raid our State and carry off our cattle. Now, thanks to the Pax Britannica, they are limited to carrying off our guests. I shall arrange an audience for you with His Highness at ten o'clock tomorrow. All you have to do is to promise faithfully to report to H.H. all the slanderous things you hear about this Court while you are the guest of the other one."

"And do I?" I asked.

"My dear sir," he said, "of course not."

I MAKE
AN UNHAPPY PRINCE
STILL MORE UNHAPPY

WITH THOSE EQUABLE WORDS in my ears, I left a happy little people and was once more concerned, indirectly, with a great one. The trouble with great nations is that the world imitates them. This would not be bad if the world imitated their virtues. But it also imitates their faults. The world cannot be blamed: a great people rarely admits to having any faults.

Now we know the illusion of one of my native lands. I shall now describe how I found that it was being copied by my other. I found this so strange that I shall describe it as it happened and my unhappy prince shall speak in his own words.

I crossed the borders of his state with high

hopes. He was a descendant of one of the greatest Indians who had ever lived—Shivaji—a thorn in the side of the English for many years and who might have driven them from the land. In the veins of my new host ran the blood of a patriot as noble as George Washington.

My new host invited me to dine with him. "Not in the palace," said the private secretary who bore the message. "His Highness says we shall dine informally in the English Cottage. That is a little private house he has built for himself in the palace grounds. Do please be absolutely informal. His Highness says it is so long since he met a young man of good education that he is longing to have a chat."

At seven in the evening I was driven in a state car to the marble doorway of a house that stretched away on either side and up into the night, and which had been built—so far as I could gather in a hasty glance—after the architectural style of the *Palazzo* of the Farnese family in Rome.

Since the evening was informal, I was invited to sit down while awaiting His Highness in the reception room, instead of standing. The court—

some fourteen people—however stood. Again, since the dinner was not official, the courtiers were dressed simply in white sherwani's, white Jodhpur breeches, embroidered slippers and jewelled buttons, instead of the formal court robes.

His Highness entered surrounded by five more superior courtiers. The party moved at a fast walk, His Highness being in the middle. To a stranger like myself the party gave the impression of an underworld king surrounded by protective henchmen. Nothing could have been further from the truth. His Highness emerged from the group and revealed himself as a charming, if stout, young man, with kindly eyes and rather too big a moustache.

He immediately said: "You must call me George. All my friends do. You really must. Now go on: call me George."

"Well, George—"

"How nicely you talk!" he went on, "you have been to school, haven't you? I bet you've been to a university, too. You're lucky. Now me, I haven't been to school at all and when I wanted to go to a university the British government said I was too ignorant. Do you like the British? So do I. But why didn't they let me be educated? After all, is it fair to stop me going to school and then say I'm ignorant? No, it isn't. I suppose they were afraid I'd be too clever, but there never was much danger of that. Do you like the British? Oh, I remember you said you did. So do I. I said that too, didn't I? I *did* say it, didn't I? Good. But I find I'm taking more and more to horses. I love horses. Do you love horses? No; I thought you might not, so I ordered dinner to be ready because that just about stumps me for conversation and I don't want to make a fool of myself. Shall we go in?"

And as we did, processionally, he said:

"An *undergrad*. Fancy having been an *undergrad*. Lucky fellow."

We entered the dining room. He sat down, I sat down, and then the court sat down, hierarchically graded round an immense table.

His Highness became gloomy with the soup.

"I see you're looking round the room," he said. "It's vulgar, isn't it? Oh, yes, it is. I know. I haven't got taste. If only I'd been given an English education like you I'd have dam' good taste. You've got taste. Oh yes you have. You're bound to have. Look

[93]

at the way you make noises when I ask you questions you don't want to answer. Like this."

He put down his spoon and made deprecating sounds.

"I can't do that, you see. If I'd have been sent to school in England I'd have been able to do it without thinking, like you. And this house wouldn't have been vulgar. It would have been in perfect English good taste."

"I'm no authority on the finer houses of England," I said. "But, to judge from those I've been allowed to enter, the architecture of the best English homes is Italian, the furniture is French, and the paintings are Dutch except for the family portraits which are done by Englishmen because foreigners don't know how to make people look respectable."

"Well, anyhow," said His Highness, "my cook is French though you wouldn't think so, would you? But then the French go to pieces in the tropics. But eat up, there's a good chap, because it goes on and on, and I want to show you my fountain. It's in the garden and there's a switchboard and we can floodlight it in six different colours. Now *that's* real vulgar, isn't it?" he said, triumphantly, and bristling his moustache at me, defied me to say it wasn't.

"Yes," I admitted, "but can *I* work the switch-board or is it reserved for you?"

"You can," he said, "but while you do it you'll have to listen to me telling you about my frustrated life. I think it's much less boring than my other conversation which is about horses, as you know, but the English don't seem to think so."

"I'm not all that English."

"So it seems. Didn't they teach you about horses at school?"

"No."

"Nor when you were an *undergrad*?"

"No."

"Funny. Anyway, eat up or we shall be here all night."

*   *   *   *   *

The fountain was commanded by switches let into the balustrade of a marble terrace. It was, in action, harmonious, beautiful and variegated. His Highness' life-story was not.

I felt some impatience with him at first. He

seemed to me to be an unusually fortunate man. He was twenty-eight and healthy. He had rank—besides his princely station he had only recently conferred upon himself a generalship in his own army —and I had only to touch a switch at my elbow to be reminded of how rich he was. His private life was happy. He had a wife who peaceably lived in the women's quarters on the top floor of the palace and asked for nothing save that His Highness should occasionally climb the stairs. As a ruler he was popular and in administration he showed distinct abilities. Observing that the natural clay of his state was good for making pottery he had set up a factory. By his princely wish the factory had concentrated on producing gnomes with red hats sitting on large toadstools, and lavatory pans—a shrewd choice since everybody with a garden could find a use for the first and everybody with a loyal heart could find a use for the second. Both products sold extremely well and the factory was promising to be a financial success. His hobby was breeding racehorses and even these sometimes won. He should have been a contented young man.

But his life had been bedevilled by an English

schoolmaster, a knight and a cynic, who had let him sip the heady wine of English gentility, but (on the advice of the India Office) had not allowed him to drain it. He had been taught to read and write. He had been taught sufficient history to despise his own people: enough geography to know that the British Empire was a considerably bigger place than his little state: and enough philosophy to keep his temper when, to the thunder of his nineteen honorific guns, he went to visit the Viceroy of India and was kept waiting twenty minutes in the anteroom.

"I'm not civilised, you see," he explained. "Try turning the midde jet pink and the side ones yellow. Nobody is who doesn't know how to behave like the English. Well, there's the Chinese. But I can't see myself arranging flowers in a corner so that they say, 'I always enjoy your company. Do come again.' That's the Japs, isn't it? I thought so. I saw a picture in the encyclopedia but I didn't read the print because it gave me a headache. I'm glad you like purple. I do too, but I don't think it's a refined colour. The Chinese go in for honourable ancestors, don't they? Right this time? Good. Well, I can't see myself with my hands tucked into my sleeves bowing to my grandfather's tablet. My ancestors weren't honourable. At least they certainly weren't gentlemen. Just rough soldiers. That's why they were able to leave me this tidy little property. Who else is there? The Americans? I've been to America. To get my teeth seen to. Everywhere I went they made me wear a funny hat just to show I wasn't stuck up. But I've got a damn sight funnier hat here than any of their cowboy Stetsons. It's red and got two horns and a couple of tassels. I wear it when I ride in state. I look like the rector's wife opening a bazaar. I've got a couple more even worse for religious ceremonies. No. If wearing funny hats is a sign of civilisation I'm as civilised as Lord Sandwich. I don't mean Sandwich, do I? I mean the man who wrote those letters that my tutor was always reading to me. That's right: Chesterfield. Thing you sit on, not thing you eat. I *must* remember. Blue makes me miserable. Cheer it up a bit, do."

Thus having introduced literature into the conversation, we talked of books, and then music and then painting; about which subjects his ignorance was such that he more nearly approached the ideal of the English gentleman than he knew.

Then he asked:

"Why did you come to India?"

"Because I am tired of the very things you admire."

"Tired?"

"They're not true. They no longer exist," I said, and I explained.

He listened to the end. He pulled out the plug of the fountain switchboard.

"So I came to India hoping that my second country would provide me with something new, and true, and of its own," I finished.

His Highness sighed.

"I understand," he said. "You mean," he went on in a dispirited voice, "you'd like to ride some elephants. I'll have them round at the guest house at six tomorrow evening if that will suit you."

At which he gave orders for the fountain to be turned off and wished me good night.

As a guest I was no doubt disappointing. But as a descendant of Shivaji, scourge of the English, so was my host.

It may be said that the illusions of one young man however well descended, are not dangerous. But all illusions are very dangerous, particularly those of national pride. Sometime later I saw the Englishman's illusion cause him to shoot a man in the belly.

THE DEAD MAN
IN THE
SILVER MARKET

SOME YEARS LATER, in the middle of the Second World War, I was walking down the Silver Market of Old Delhi when I heard the sound of firing. Making my way towards it I turned a corner and came upon a small crowd defying an even smaller band of English soldiers. An elderly man of the poorest class, dressed only in a loin cloth, broke away from the crowd and ran towards the soldiers. One of these pointed an automatic weapon towards him, but the man did not stop. He was shouting in a confused and hysterical manner and it seemed to me that he was not in possession of his senses; no doubt as so often happens with Indians, the excitement and the previous shooting had loosened his grip upon his nerves. He ran on, full tilt towards the soldiers. The Englishman with the automatic weapon pressed the trigger and the Indian fell prone, jerking his legs in a fashion that was almost ludicrous and drumming with his fists on the ground. In a few moments he lay still, dead, with blood spouting from a series of wounds in his body. I noticed that the small of his back (for he died on his face) was torn in several places from the bullets which had passed through.

The crowd dispersed. They had been demanding that the English leave India. The man lay in the roadway in his blood, until a street-cleaning cart, requisitioned for the purpose, bore him away.

* * * * *

By a chance which was not remarkable I met one of the soldiers who had been in the party that had done the shooting. He was brought to my house by a friend who sought entertainment for English soldiers. He brought five or six, chosen from a list with a pin and one of them was this young man.

He was square-faced, short, and agreeable in his manner, though rough, in the style of the streets rather than the barracks. He remembered the incident of the shooting well. It arose in the conversation by accident and to his great amusement he said that he had at last 'tumbled to where he had seen me before.'

It appeared that when the firing started I had taken refuge in a small public latrine made of sheet iron and stakes. He had observed this, and it had made him laugh.

I asked him where his home town was and he told me that it was an industrial slum near Liverpool. He was much attached to it. He described with nostalgia a road called 'The Gut' which ran from the brass foundry to the railway bridge and had fourteen public houses. Here the boys would whistle at the girls or buy them fried fish. He himself was something of a leader of his generation. They had formed a gang that took its pleasure in brushes with the police: they committed little crimes and ran away, the police after them. Sometimes they were caught, but not often. He had been bound over to keep the peace on one occasion and, on another, let off by the magistrate with a warning. This leniency was allowed him because he was about to go to war. He had been drafted to India. The shooting in the Silver Market was the first action he had seen.

One of his soldier companions said:

"Well, I'm——glad I missed that——show. Poor bastards. Some of them haven't got a rag to cover their arses."

At which the soldier from the slums squared his shoulders.

"I dunno so much," he said.

His companion said:

"What d'yer mean, 'You dunno so much?' "

"I mean," said the first soldier, "we've got t' keep Law an' Order."

I said:

"Those people you shot at in the Silver Market think they can keep law and order for themselves."

"They *think*," he said. "It takes more than thinkin'. They might, if we learned 'em 'ow to do it for an 'undred years or so. But then, I dunno." He pulled on his cigarette and disengaged some tobacco from his lower lip with a neat movement of his tongue. "Seems t'me, that sort of thing ain't learned. It's bred in yer bones."

The successor to the oligarchs, the heir to Lord Curzon, Clive and General Wellesley being a soldier in uniform, I changed the subject of the conversation by serving more whiskey.

THE LAST NABOB

WHILE ONE ENGLISH SOLDIER was sufficient to shoot one coolie, the number of English soldiers required to shoot all the coolies in India was beyond the means of the imperial Exchequer: and it was becoming clear that nothing less would do.

Millions of Indians, urged by the example and advice of Mahatma Gandhi, were defying the soldiery by non-violent means, sitting in front of them and singing Hindu, Mohammedan and Christian hymns. Among these was 'Onward Christian Soldiers,' which thus took on a meaning never intended by the composers.

Other Indians, equally convinced of the moral grandeur of non-violence, had made up their minds that it was a creed which one day all the world would adopt, but probably not before a dead soldier arose from the battlefield to continue the fight.

These were busy de-railing trains, burning police stations and stealing arms.

It was broadly obvious that a period of history was at its end. Since I have traced, if only briefly, the story of the people who dominated that period, I shall now draw the portrait of the last of them as I saw him.

* * * * *

While the oligarchy was refreshed, as I have said, by marriage with the lower orders, there grew up in the nineteenth century another system, small in extent but very useful. Readers of Thackeray will know it well. By this system an Englishman spent several years in the East gathering money. He returned to England with a bad liver but a large fortune. He was accepted into the oligarchy, after some delay to cool him off. He was popularly called a Nabob. This somewhat contemptuous title was later dropped in favour of regular knighthoods awarded by the Throne in India, which hurried up the Nabob's acceptance into English society a good deal. An Indian knighthood was certainly not as good as a metropolitan one. But the whole lot were indiscriminately called 'Sir' and this was what really counted.

* * * * *

In the Middle Ages before a man was made a knight he was required to watch his armour, on his knees in a church, for the whole period between dusk and dawn.

In Imperial India his wait was longer but much more comfortable. Most of the Empire knights watched and prayed for fifteen years before the honour was granted them. During this time only two things were expected of them by the advisors to the Throne: they must make money and must not involve themselves openly with coloured women. The first of these tests of worthiness was easy to pass. An Englishman in a good position with an ear of authority did not have to seek money in Imperial India; he had it thrust upon him. The second test, however, was often quite a pitfall.

If he passed it, or was not widely known to have failed it, and if he amassed sufficient money, he passed into the concluding stages of his vigil. These were more difficult but he was sustained through

them by other Empire knights who guided him on
the way he should go.

Ever since chivalry began, a new knight had to
perform some quite unselfish act of public service.
In India, this was cautiously exacted before the
honour was bestowed. The candidate was not expected to think of an unselfish act himself. It was
recognised that making money, though easy in
India, drives even the best men into set ways. The
candidate would therefore be invited to dine with
the Governor, perforce a man already dubbed and
knowing the ropes. Over the brandy the floodgates
of pity and compassion would be deftly opened in
the candidate's breast and broad hints dropped as to
the direction in which the balm should flow.

Next, the candidate's wife was obliged to give a
number of small receptions at which the aspirant
was closely observed by the older hands, to see if
he would 'do.' I cannot say what 'doing' meant
in a positive way: that is the mystery of the body
of the Knights of the Indian Empire. But it was
well-known that the candidate's conversation should
not show too close an acquaintance with contem-
porary literature, with Indian politics, with religion,

or with any of the three hundred and a half million inhabitants of the sub-continent except his body-servant about whom he should be very enthusiastic. It would sound easy, but it was not. Deprived of so many topics of conversation, the poor man might easily talk about the thing in which he had spent his life—his business: and 'shop' was anathema.

But if he could manage to convey the impression that he had never earned a penny yet had somehow salted away a comfortable fortune, he passed. He was called to Viceroy's House. The ceremony, I am told, was simple, but I cannot believe that it was. The mere touch of a dress-sword could scarcely work such a change in a man's personality as I have observed in new-dubbed knights. I cannot account for it, unless the sword is anointed, and a potion slipped into the knight by means of some playful poke on the part of an affable Crown. But this is improbable.

I was not able to study the rise of a knight in the great days: and it cannot be learned from documents. There could not be less written about the process if the knights had stolen their stars instead of being given them in a box. However I knew one knight of these latter times well: he may not be typical: but he was almost certainly the last. His dubbing was left so late that when he went to receive his honour his friends were uncertain whether he would come back Sir William Ponder, or a Pandit. But just because he was the last addition that India had made to the English oligarchy he has all of the interest of sunset and the dying fall.

* * * * *

William Ponder (as I shall call him) was forty-two when I first met him. He was short and already stout. He had the large dull face of a man who is good at arithmetic.

This ability to add up, subtract and do long division had been his special talent ever since he was a schoolboy, and his only one. His parents had been proud of him and they had sent him to private school. There, to judge from others who had been classmates, little William had been present at lessons in Latin, French, history, geography, literature, drawing and something called science. But one only had to listen to William's mature conversation—or rather the echoing silences with which he strewed it—to know that all this instruction ran off William's back. He merely got better and better at arithmetic.

His parents wisely decided that a university had nothing to teach their clever son; when he left school they articled him to a chartered accountant. So far as I know, or any of Ponder's friends in India know, this was the last thing they did in their lives. Ponder mentioned his parents as any man must. But beyond those three things—they were proud of him, they had sent him to a good school, and they had paid for him to be articled—he said nothing about them at all. When I knew him, the Advisors to the Throne already had their eye on him as a possible knight, and Ponder was aware of it. So I imagine Ponder's silence was due to his parents having kept a shop.

Perhaps it was this that made him choose his Bombay apartment so that its balcony overlooked a swimming pool. Few people would deliberately prefer to live within easy reach of the splashes and shouts and confusions of such a place. But this pool was in a sense the heart of the Indian Empire. Nobody could swim in it who was not a European.

I should explain that the word *European* substantially meant *English*. But if the pool had been strictly closed to anybody but the English, the Americans would have been barred as well. This would have been awkward, so the word *European* was coined as a gesture, however carefully measured, in their direction. This had the disadvantage of letting in the Latin consular officials and their wives. But this misfortune was accepted resignedly as unavoidable; no undue fuss ever was made about it.

The English community defended its action in closing the baths to Indians, but I do not know that any Indian ever attacked it. Among the Hindus, those who might have felt hurt—the upper castes— felt, on the contrary, quite sympathetic. They themselves would view with horror and loathing the prospect of getting into water which already held an Englishman. As for the lower castes, they would not have been particular. But they, too, were disgusted that there was no rule to prevent women using the water every day in the month, if they so desired. All told, the pool performed its function— which was to inflame the Englishman's racial pride while cooling his skin—without causing much bad blood.

Ponder used it often, though he was no swimmer, and he was able to look at it all his leisure hours. No doubt the sight of it helped him over those awkward minutes with his English friends when conversation turned on *home*. Ponder trod carefully during these times, not always with complete success. But it must have been reassuring for him, when his friends had made their slightly too affable farewells, to look down at the pool and feel that however much he might be out of it in London—Ponder had no club: Ponder had no 'place in the country': Ponder had, it seemed no friends at *home*—nevertheless here, he was literally and undeniably in the swim.

His worst moments came when he was forced to say why he had left *home* and come to India. In the Imperial days which I am recalling, every Englishman had a formal reason for his coming out East. Nobody said that they had come to India because the country and its people attracted them, for the very good reason, I believe, that it would not have been true. Nobody said that they came because they could not get a good job in London: for the equally good reason that for many of them it scarcely needed saying. The best formal reason was that their family had 'connections with India.' They had been there before, in the Army, in Government, or best of all, with John Company. This was a very good reason because it made one's sojourn in India something that one could not escape, an inherited but not disgraceful disease, like gout. Next in favour came the reason that one was a younger son and "I didn't see myself in a dog-collar." This meant that the speaker was given the choice of becoming a clergyman or going out East. Then there were a series of less good reasons ending in very dubious ones, like having to learn the business before becoming a London director: but none were so thoroughly bad as Ponder's. He would say, in his hesitating, unsure way:

"Well, you see, I didn't mean to come, you understand? But the partners—old friends, you know, of my people—my parents, that is—the partners saw that I was *unhappy*. You see what I mean? They saw I was unhappy and they thought I might like India—that is—a change might do me good and they wanted a good man out here because their old *burra sahib* had drunk himself—I mean, he was just about on his last legs. So I came." He would end, lamely and disastrously. In the minds of his listeners there was only one reason that an Englishman could be suspected of liking India more than Home and that was an irrepressible sexual desire for dark skins. Had Ponder ever shown the slightest urge in that direction he would have been ruined. Fortunately he showed no urges of that sort in any direction whatever: not even, it was said, in the direction of the pale and fretful Mrs. Ponder, so he was saved.

Nor did his story fit his personality. It was difficult to imagine Ponder suffering so deep an emotion as unhappiness. If he had ever done so, the cause must have been extraordinary, and the impression remained with his listeners that unless the 'partners' had beaten and starved their apprentice, they must have had some reason other than unhappiness for sending him abroad. I suppose the truth was that Ponder found himself one day in urgent need of money: and maybe the partners were glad to be rid of him. Ponder's dull face may well have been a reminder, day in and day out, that personalities do not blossom in their profession. If that was the case, it should have been easy for Ponder to think up a better lie. Maybe he had tried, but his mind had refused to do anything but mental arithmetic.

In palmier days he would have been left to make his Indian fortune in peace. He would have retired and gone to live in England, plain Mr. William Ponder, of Cheltenham, who had a fire lit in his bedroom from September to the end of May, but was otherwise indistinguishable from other retired gentlemen. He would never have been one of those who return from India a new member of the English ruling class. But by the time that Ponder had reached middle age, observant Englishmen in the know saw that the system of raising selected commoners to the knighthood and thus refreshing the oligarchy back Home had come to an end. This meant that somebody had to be the Last Knight. For an imperially-minded Englishman there was something solemn about the thought of the last recipient of an honour that had been awarded for a century: perhaps, too, it had a subtle appeal to their English sense of the ludicrous. They might have

He was fond of saying that the Governor was the easiest Englishman to talk to he had ever met in India. This might well have been true. Ponder's lack of a secure past exactly matched the Governor's lack of any foreseeable future.

There was, besides, another reason. English Governors were supposed to maintain themselves above politics. This one was so far above them that he once asked at his dinner table what exactly was the difference between the points of view of Mohammed Ali Jinnah and Mahatma Gandhi. Later, he thought it wiser to cover his very human ignorance and he took to playing the bagpipes after dinner to entertain his guests. A more effective way to avoid answering—or asking—embarrassing questions has never been invented. But it must have left a yearning in the Governor to have a safe gossip once in a while. For this, Ponder was admirable. If it were possible, he knew even less about India than the Governor.

With the help of his new friend, Ponder set about making himself a gentleman, at a quick trot. Time was short. English statesmen were visiting Delhi at ever-shortening intervals assuring Indians that nothing held them back from freedom save their own divisions. They invited Indians to find some common basis of agreement and locked up the leaders of the principal party in jail, possibly to secure them peace and quiet for reflection. When the people came out on the streets and built barricades, they let the leaders out again, this being the only way left to get the people to go back to their homes. The Governor, serene, played, 'The Campbells are Coming,' after his dinner parties, but nobody had much faith in the Campbells.

The end, it was felt, was very near. One day, when there was no transport on the streets, Ponder gave me a lift in his car. We rounded a corner and ran into a barricade of oil-drums and torn-down tramway standards. Young Indians in Gandhi caps made Ponder get down and shout, 'Jai Hind,' the war-cry of the rebellion. Ponder shouted obligingly, treating the thing, like all the other English residents, as a game of forfeits, as indeed it was, the biggest game of forfeits that the English had ever played.

When he got back in the car, I could see what progress he had made in his education. He was calm and collected. All that remained of the old Ponder was a heavy dew of sweat on his upper lip and a nervous little sniff.

"We ought to go," he said. "We ought to tell 'em we're going straight away. Then they'd come on their bended knees to us and ask us to stay. Who's going to defend them? We've got the Army and the Navy and the Air-force. They're *facts*. When they see those packing up and leaving they'll know what a lot of agitators have led them into." He sniffed. Then the seedling gentleman wilted a little. "See what I mean?" he said.

On the day his wife gave her first party for the inspection of her husband, the Indian Navy mutinied. It seized the barracks and trained its ships' guns on the principal buildings of the city. Ponder was now becoming a gentleman, not at a trot, but at a good steady gallop. Some Indian officials were asked to the party—perhaps in the hope that if the shooting started they would act like the sign on the door that the Angel made at Passover—and I was asked, too, my function on such occasions being to talk to the Indians in case nobody else should.

Ponder did well, if breathlessly. His rooms held a bookcase. He denied all knowledge of the books in them and said that they were his wife's. He had had a taste for Chinese celadon ware in the days before his elevation and he had collected some good pieces. Although he would never have been allowed a liking for books, I think he could have got away with collecting Chinese pottery. It was a thing they did in English country houses. But Ponder was taking no risks with art. When I admired his plates, he said a friend had dumped the lot on him when leaving for home, and was amusedly surprised when told that they were valuable. He never mentioned money, figures or arithmetic. He never once asked anybody if they saw what he meant. In any case it was quite clear. He meant to make the grade.

The mutineers did not discharge their guns. But Mrs. Ponder fired a broadside of her own. While the mutineers were hauling down their red, white and green flags under promise of an amnesty, Mrs. Ponder ran off with an Air-force sergeant who in civilian life was an actor in a stock-company in England. She set up an apartment with him under

Ponder's nose. She meant to ruin her husband. She failed. The English community, and especially that section of it which was known to be in touch with Government House, hushed the matter up. It was felt that the times were too risky to display such a bad example to the natives. It was a tradition that the Indians were held down less by force of arms than by the moral splendour of the occupying English, and this was more than ever necessary now, when the British armed forces were busy in Europe and in Burma. The charge against Mrs. Ponder was not so much that she had deserted her husband's bed, but that she had deserted it in the face of the enemy.

* * * * *

The pace grew hotter. There was a riot in some part of Bombay every second day. We were put under a curfew from dusk to dawn. Troops opened fire with machine-guns in the centre of the city and killed several rioters. The Governor cancelled all evening parties.

During these days it was my custom to go to the Taj Mahal Hotel at eleven o'clock and meet a young Indian woman of exceptional intelligence. In common with several other Indians in the know, we had laid bets on Ponder. I said he would get his knighthood. The young woman, much more fervid a patriot than myself, said he would not. She put up her money but said it was a shame to rob me of mine: nobody would dare make knights with people lying dead in the streets. I said that if she thought that, she might as well lengthen the odds. We had just settled them when we saw Ponder through a window, walking.

Obviously, he was in distress. Englishmen did not walk in the streets during midday hours. They rode in automobiles. Besides, Ponder was in a beautiful suit. It was light grey, and clearly cut by the only English tailor left in India. He was also wearing pretty hand-made shoes, and a tie with bands of symbolic colours. In a word, he was dressed to the eyes in the uniform of a gentleman. The Lord Chancellor crossing Piccadilly in full-bottomed wig and brocaded gown could not have been more incongruous than Ponder walking a Bombay street in such a dress.

We hammered on the window. He turned his

face towards us, and we saw that he was red and sweating. He came inside. I introduced him to my friend and Ponder fumbled and averted his eyes while shaking hands, it being a long tradition that 'one did not look at Their womenfolk because They might feel insulted.'

We asked where he was walking to. Government House, he told us. He had a lunch appointment. But just as he was leaving his office, his chauffeur had told him that somebody had slashed all four tyres of his car and written 'Go back' on the paint-work. Then the driver had disappeared. There were no taxis, no victorias, nothing. They were shooting again at Bori Bunder. He was desperate. So he had begun to walk.

"Couldn't you ring up the Governor and say you can't come?" I asked. He looked at me with his dull face that now seemed proper on top of such a suit of clothes.

"One doesn't," he said.

This was an exquisite remark, for it showed that Ponder's education had progressed at a hot-house rate. He now looked upon himself as one of the Ones. I said nothing in reply. I waited to see if, to pile pleasure on pleasure, he would ask me if I saw what he meant. He did, but his little phrase had undergone a metamorphosis.

"One doesn't," he repeated, *"d'you know."*

I was glad that he was rewarded for this triumph of re-education. The young woman offered him a lift in her car.

"They're pulling Europeans out of them, I'm told," she said. "But Menen can look out of one window and I'll look out of the other and you can sit in the middle, and my driver's practically coal-black, so you should be quite safe."

So he was, but he did not sit in the middle all the way. We were stopped at Bori Bunder by an English picket. Some of them were sprawled on the pavement by a machine-gun. Others were turning away traffic. The vast square was quite empty except for a small group of young men in *dhotis* and Gandhi caps who were peering at the soldiers from an alleyway.

The sergeant came to my side of the car.

"Where yer going?"

He was a hot, tired Cockney. His bush-shirt was black with sweat. His pale face showed that he had not been in the Indian Empire more than a few days.

"Government House."

"Got any pipers?"

"No," but there was a bustle and a heave beside me. Ponder had papers: or rather one—his invitation card.

The sergeant took it and read the copper-plate, word for word. Then he looked at Ponder, at Ponder's tie, at Ponder's waistcoat and lastly, leaning forward slightly to do it, at Ponder's pretty hand-made shoes.

"I don't think you'll make it,"—a pause—"sir. They've just behaved very nasty to an Englishman down the road. Very nasty."

"It's all right, officer," the young girl said. "We'll be responsible for him. If there's any trouble I can talk to them,"—a pause from the woman as ironic as the sergeant's—"in their own lingo, you know."

"Well, I dunno as I can allow . . ."

"But you must," said Ponder. "We can't give way to them."

The sergeant wiped his lips with the back of his

hand and then wiped the back of his hand on his shirt, all very slowly. No words could have made it more clear that he, for his part, was ready to give way to a boy with a peashooter, if it could be squared with his orders. Then he said:

"All right. On you go. But," and he handed back the invitation card, "I'll 'ave to ask you to lie on the floor—sir. I can't have you taking risks."

Ponder got down on the mat. At first he sat. But when we left the square and were out of range of the picket's machine-gun, we found the crowd that they had been shooting at. When we were forced to slow down, and some of the demonstrators approached the car, Ponder followed the sergeant's instruction to the foot of the letter.

The young woman and I leaned out of the window of the car, waving, asking questions, hailing Mother India, and giving all the information we knew and much we did not about the situation in other parts of the city. The driver slowly increased his pace until we bowled clear of the crowd and away.

Ponder did not ask if he could get up and we did not invite him to do so. We carried him, recumbent, to the gateway of Government House. The car stopped and Ponder got out. Getting out of a car from a position on the floor, if it is to be done with dignity, needs more thought and planning than Ponder was able to give it. But the sentries saluted him very smartly.

* * * * *

They made him a K.C.I.E. The 'K' stood for knight, the 'C' for Commander and the 'I.E.' for nothing at all: by the time Ponder's envelopes were coming in with the correct form of address, the Indian Empire had gone to join such episodes in English history as child labour, the persecution of the Quakers and the Liverpool slave market—things which as I was taught at school show the greatness of the English character because they have stopped doing them.

FAKIRS—THEN AND NOW

THE BEST THING that can be said of the British Raj in India is that a great number of Indians barely knew it existed. In wide areas of India the Raj did not so much govern the people: it refrained from raising any objection to their existence. It was a tyranny—by which I mean the rulers made their own laws to suit their own purposes—but tyrannies are not always so nonchalant, and this should fairly be recognised.

We have seen a state which was untroubled by the English. I will now describe a community that was equally unconcerned with them, or nearly so. These were the fakirs.

* * * *

It should be explained at once that a fakir is as normal a figure in the public life of India as a Senator is in America. He is as easy to meet and when met is not looked upon as being any more bizarre.

Like the Senator, he is a member of an envied profession; but he is perhaps regarded with more affection. To the common man of India a fakir is an escape from the dull round of seed-time and harvest, death and procreation. They are his head-line personalities, and just as the Western man follows the fortunes of some tennis player or boxer, or indeed any athlete who can hit a man or a ball harder than anyone else so the man-in-the-village-street follows the exploits of Ramakrishnan who buries himself alive for a month, Mahadev who swings from a pole supported by nothing more than a hook through his chin, or Gurushankar who once sat still for twenty-three years.

But all fakirs are not gymnosophists, just as all idols in the West are not men of muscle. Without drawing the comparison too fine one might say that there are fakirs who are the equivalent of motion picture celebrities: people who possess some knack of charm or attraction, such as the well-known fakir who is ninety years old and has never washed.

In all religions there are saints who live uncomfortable lives and saints who are jolly. The public likes both sorts and so they do in India. There are fakirs, for example, who have pictures painted on one foot to show that they have never set it on the ground. On the other hand, there are fakirs who are merely quiet old gentlemen who tell their beads. Both may be equally revered. Indeed both may be equally holy: saintliness is the most chancy of professions.

But this is changing and very fast. Even as I write it may no longer be true. When India was a subject land, the fakirs went quietly about the country, sticking pins in themselves or chanting prayers, and minding their own business. No sooner was the first all-Indian Government installed in New Delhi than a patriotic section of the fakir's profession came to the city of Bombay and staged a week's demonstration on the beach. While the gymnosophists performed unheard-of austerities, others burned unparalleled quantities of melted butter upon an inferno of sacrificial fires. They were persuading the gods to make peace between the nations. In interviews with the Press, they declared that India, for millennia the most civilised

nation on earth, was now free, and she had a duty
to lead mankind to a better world.

* * * * *

I was very struck by this. I wished to know
more but the crowd round the beach numbered
half a million persons and I could not even see the
ceremonies, much less study this new example of
national pride.

But after the peacemakers had gone, I went on
a journey into the country and there I discovered
a temple area in which I could meet fakirs not only
at my leisure but at theirs. This temple area was
principally a large square swimming pool (called
a 'tank') with steps leading into the water and a
paved walk on all four sides. Lining the outer edge
of the paved walk were various small temples,
cheek by jowl. At the entrance to this sacred enclosure was a small plot of ground with some trees—
for holy men who preferred to sit under trees—and
here fakirs would meet.

Since all this may seem strange to a Western
reader, I shall describe what I found with due attention to atmosphere and detail. I shall introduce

him to three fakirs—the first two will demonstrate what they were; the last will serve to show what many of them have become.

* * * * *

My first acquaintance was Pandit Mahadev, an educated and polite man of some fifty years, smeared with cow dung ash and sporting a large white moustache. He habitually sat under the first tree on one's left as one entered the enclosure.

For my initial visits I did no more than salute him, and then made my way to some temple or other where I paid a priest to hammer on a bell. He was always busy cooking something in a pot over a small fire.

On my third visit he read my palm in a desultory fashion and then said, "You are a . . ." He paused and I said:

"A writer."

"So I thought," he said. "You are at the moment engaged on a work about . . ."

"Holy men," I said.

"As anyone can see from your palm," he went on.

Easy relations having been thus established between us I was able to ask him many questions. He readily answered them, and in the course of several more visits we became old friends.

I asked him one day about the food in his perennially boiling pot:

"Is all your food given to you?" I asked. He nodded, and I commented at such a convenient method of keeping house.

"It is really nothing so very extraordinary," said the Guru. "Elsewhere in the world professors and learned men are paid salaries with which they buy food. Here we make matters a little more simple. That is really all there is to it."

I asked him further:

"Do you teach? Do you give lectures to the people who buy you this food?"

At this point his little pot began to splutter and the Pandit gave it his attention. He said to me, in a kindly but preoccupied fashion:

"If you go over to the white stone you're bound to find somebody putting down an offering. They'll tell you all about it."

He poked around in the pot and blew up his

little fire in an irritated manner. I judged it best to
follow his advice and leave him to his cooking for
a while. On the edge of the clearing round the tree
was a stone about three feet high that had been
whitewashed. A tall peasant with a handsome but
vacant face was laying out fruit on its top. I went
over to him and he gave me a deep salute. I returned this clumsily.

"These are for the Pandit?" I said.

"Yes, if he'll take them."

"Do you want him to pray for you?"

The tall peasant straightened himself up and
looked more handsome and more vacant than ever.

"Pray, sahib? *Pray*? Why should I want him to
pray for me?"

"Isn't that why you give him the fruit?"

"Oh, no." He paused. He looked across to where
the Pandit squatted over his pot. The peasant
lowered his voice. "All I want is to stop him
cursing me. He's the cleverest devil in the whole
Tank. Has he told you what he was before he came
here? He was a *vakil*."

This meant that the Pandit had been a lawyer.

"And he was making enough money at it to

buy up our whole village. He saved three men from hanging and jailed I don't know how many. Oh, he's clever all right. No beating him."

"Still, why should he curse you?"

"Why not?" said the peasant. "Why should a clever chap like that wish any good to an ordinary plain fool peasant like me?" Then sketching a salute, he went away.

When I returned to the tree the Pandit was blowing mightily at his fire and he did not break the rhythm of his puffs while saying:

"Ah (phooh-huh!), there you are (phooh-huh!). *That* surprised you (hoooohf!), I'll bet."

"He said he was afraid you'd curse him."

"So I would (phoof!) I daresay, if I knew (pooff!) how to do it. There, it's going nicely at last."

He sat back, his cheeks pink with blowing, and he grinned at me.

"What did he say about me?"

"He said you were a clever devil."

"So I am."

"He said you were a *vakil*."

"So I was."

"Why did you give it up?"

"Well, now, have I given it up? That's the question. When I was a lawyer, young fellows like that one, who got into trouble used to pay me thousands of rupees to defend them. You see I had a reputation of not doing it unless I was paid a fat fee. The gallows is as good a machine as the rack to threaten a man with."

"And you had that on your conscience, so you gave it all up?" I suggested.

"My conscience? Well, now, I wonder. People say that great criminal lawyers—I was called that y'know—they say that great criminal lawyers haven't got a conscience. I don't think that's quite true. I certainly had a conscience and I used to examine it very strictly. But whatever the charge I brought against it, I was such a good lawyer I could always secure an acquittal. And I'm afraid it's much the same with most members of my profession. The reason for my giving up the bar and doing this,"—and he indicated his ash-marks—"was quite different. Almost commonplace, you might say, at least for India. My young brother fell very ill and I made a vow that if he got well again I would make a pilgrimage as a mendicant to Benares. My father had done it. He left home with one rupee, got safely to Benares and returned by train, first class, paying his fare with the money he'd got out of people on his way. And so I did it too, because my brother recovered. I set out for Benares with one rupee and I got here without any undue difficulty. That was about ten years ago."

"And you didn't go any further?"

"No."

"Why?"

He lowered his head, studied the ground, and stayed in this posture for some considerable time, deep in thought. Finally he raised his face to mine and beaming, said:

"I liked the life."

It will be seen that the Pandit was the old-style simple type of fakir. But he was not at all famous. Of the simple, but famous, Big Tim was a good instance. I do not know his proper name because I could never properly catch all its syllables and I never saw it written down in English. It ended in the syllable Tim. So much as I could catch. And Tim was undeniably big. He was introduced to me by my friend the Pandit after the Pandit had entertained me one day to a breakfast of bananas and some soured milk which I drank from a gleaming brass pot. When I had finished he took me for a walk round the "Tank."

We had gone scarcely ten yards along the East side when we came across Big Tim leaning his great length against one of the pillars that are slotted for oil-lamps, and which make a pyramid of fire on the festival of Divali. Big Tim was wearing a loose robe that fell to his ankles. It opened to show his chest, rather like a bathing wrap—he was in fact thinking of taking a ceremonial dip—and I could see that he was of a mountainous build.

The Pandit went up to him and looked absurdly small. He told Big Tim who I was and he told me Big Tim's name. Big Tim moved his position very slightly and turned his enormous oval head in my direction. He smiled in a serious way. On being first introduced to an elephant only the most collected person thinks of patting its trunk. As for me, I was thoroughly put out and pushed my right hand forward in the English fashion, although I should have remembered to fold my hands in front of my face. Big Tim put out his own right hand, seized mine and held it in his own, where it lay entrapped like a mouse in some flesh-eating tropical plant. As is so often the way with large men when embarrassed, he simpered.

"Big Tim," said the Pandit (although he used, of course, his proper name), "is just the man I wanted you to meet. He is one of our most famous men. He is perhaps the best-known naked fakir in India."

"Oh yes?" I said.

"You understand what I mean? He goes stark naked." Big Tim, still holding my hand was looking from one of us to the other in an uncomprehending manner and the Pandit said to him in one of the easier common languages of India:

"I was just explaining to the gentleman here that you go naked."

Big Tim said in the same lingua franca, and to me:

"But only in public."

"Oh, of course," I said, and we all sat down on the top step of the 'Tank.'

Two or three devotees were taking their morning bath in a very pretty fashion. They walked slowly down the steps into the water which rose slowly to their waists (since the steps continued well beneath the water). They then, all together, scooped some water into their cupped hands and flung it forwards, saying prayers. Next they moved down two or three more steps, clearing away the lotus-leaves that lay on the surface of the water by swinging their hands and their bodies in wide arcs from left to right and back again. All this looked very fine in the morning sun. When the water was up to their necks, they raised their arms into the air and sang a hymn.

* * * * *

The Pandit asked Big Tim to explain to me exactly what he did and Big Tim tried. But he was hamstrung in his attempts at the outset because he could not honestly see that there was anything to explain. To put one's self in Big Tim's position one must imagine oneself as slow in speech, not given to conversation, and having to explain to a Matabele why one wears a collar and tie.

"There are a lot of us," he said, "who don't wear any clothes. I mean I'm not the only one."

And when he saw from the Pandit's expression that this was scarcely good enough he struggled a step further.

"It's been going on a long time," he said apologetically.

"About three thousand years," the Pandit intervened impatiently, "but this gentleman wants to know what you *do*. He has an enquiring mind and he wants to find out all he can about his fatherland." He added here an admirably brief summary of my background. "So you can see, we ought to help him all we can, if only so that he can correct all those silly notions about us. I've told him a lot but I am really only on the fringe of things. Now you are a real fakir. So be a good chap," (or 'be a fine fellow' or 'be a stalwart,' if you prefer it; I am trying to translate his vernacular with English vernacular) "be a good chap and tell him what you do."

Big Tim nodded slowly and several times. Then swaying his body towards me like a falling tower he said:

"Well you see, I go naked."

I nodded.

"I don't say I like going naked. Then again, I

don't say I don't like it." He stopped. "You follow me?" he enquired anxiously.

"You mean you don't really care one way or another," I said.

"*That's* it," he said. "That's just it," and he gazed at me for a moment clearly admiring my quickness of wit. "It's the women who like it."

"Oh," I said. "Oh, yes, of course."

Here the Pandit took over the explanation as it had been obvious that he wanted to do from the very moment it began.

"You mustn't be misled by Big Tim's simple way of putting things. Big Tim is a simple thinker: and after all, why not? His is a very simple way of life. In fact it is difficult to think of one more simple. All he does is to take off his clothes and walk in a procession. Of course there are prayers and so forth, but we all say prayers and it comes as a second nature in time, like breathing. As for the women, well, Big Tim's reputation is made entirely by them, as you will understand when I describe the procession to you which I shall do straight away if Big Tim wouldn't mind stepping in if I get any of the details wrong."

The processions, he explained take place several times a year and all over the country. There is no fixed calendar (here Big Tim said that he didn't know about a calendar but they always had a procession after the rains) and the ceremony took place virtually when enough naked fakirs were gathered together to make a passable display.

They would then meet at an early hour in some temple precincts or the borders of a 'Tank' such as the one we were in, and they would say some prayers. They then took off their clothes and formed a procession. Should the fancy take any of them to do so they might twine flowers in their hair. But this was usually considered proper only for the younger fakirs. The elder ones—and there were naked fakirs of eighty and ninety who had been processioning all their lives—put on a little ashes and cow-dung and nothing more.

Attendants, clothed, would blow on conch-shells and beat gongs. The devotees would strike up an anthem and the whole procession would wind out of the temple into the public streets.

These would be lined with spectators, among them many women. The men in the watching crowd would regard the spectacle purely as an entertainment, though they would not, whatever the temptation, be irreverent. Those of the women who were barren or desired a child would watch the procession with passionate intensity. It was a fertility rite.

Later, when the procession had got back to the temple, the women would come to some secluded grove nearby and the fakirs would sit round in state, reading (if they could read), muttering prayers or telling their large carved wooden beads. The unfertile women would then touch their organs of generation and go away in the belief that their ritual act had given them the fecundity they sought.

The virtue thus transferred could, in theory, flow from any naked devotee, however old. There was (so the Pandit said) some feeling that the rite was more refined if the woman selected a venerable and bearded fakir. The essence of the thing was the worship of the god. Everything else was only an outward show and symbol of the inner piety.

But human nature being what it is the outward show and symbol often had more importance in people's eyes than the theological background. Old men were sought out for the blessings: the younger ones for their virility. As these latter moved about the country their reputation would precede them: and it was a fact (so I was assured) that the god did grant fertility to those who favoured his disciples.

The younger men with big reputations were surrounded by flattery and applause, and the more greedy among them could demand and get food and money and even (so illogical is the pious mind) sumptuous clothing. Some of them grew vain under all this attention and put on the airs of prima donnas. Others, like Big Tim, remained modest. Big Tim's reputation as a miracle worker, nevertheless, stood as high as anyone's, and in certain areas where he had been particularly efficacious, it stood above all his rivals. The processions in which he took part were extremely elaborate. Old men were proud to be seen in them, and younger aspirants felt that it was a step in their career. When these had all defiled in front of the eager spectators, singing and chanting, Big Tim's appearance at the tail of the procession, walking alone with a clear space all round was, the Pandit assured me, something of a *coup de theâtre*.

* * * * *

My first conversation with Big Tim had to be cut short for I had other business: but I spoke with him on very many other occasions and he became quite a friend. He had a simple kindliness that was very attractive. I asked him a good many questions. One of the things I was most curious to know was whether the processions and their subsequent ritual ever led to any scandals.

Big Tim, when his tongue was a little loosened by familiarity with me, answered me very equably. He was always even-tempered with me, and I think he was much the same with everybody else. It came from the fact that he had quite made up his mind that he had everything he needed in life.

"Oh, yes," he said. "There *are* scandals. Quite a lot."

There was nobody in the 'Tank' on this particular morning and Big Tim was skimming flat stones across the water. It was a game he was fond of and it was a complicated form of 'Ducks and Drakes.'

Not only did one have to make one's stone hop three times, but one of the hops had to be over a specified clump of lotus plants. The challenger skimmed and straddled a particular bunch with four stones one after the other; the other player had to take in that bunch in his own throws.

"Some of our people," said Big Tim, filling in his usual long pauses with throws, "do—well—just what you'd—think—and—" he paused for a long while during which he made a beautiful cast, "—they don't wait for the god to take action but do it themselves. Get's us all—a bad—name."

He challenged me to throw stones. I tried, and failed to hop the lotus bunch. He said:

"Well, I've been doing this a lot longer than you have, so you mustn't be disappointed. I can't—think—why they do it."

"You mean—why they go with the women?"

"Yes," said Big Tim, with little frowns of bewilderment. "I don't see it myself, women never did interest me very much."

"No?"

"No. We take a vow of chastity—" he stopped.

"Go on."

"You won't be interested."

"Oh yes I will be."

"It's not interesting really. All I wanted to say was that—I find—the vow—easy to keep. Those other fellows seem to want to make life a lot more difficult than it need be. *Shabash!*" he said, congratulating me on a lucky throw and thus ending what must have seemed, to him, a lengthy oration.

* * * * *

Not all the fakirs had Big Tim's pellucid character. The longer I knew Big Tim the more I liked him. But some of the others were different and after meeting them, I avoided their company.

There was one such man called Ramchandra. He had held his right arm above his head for twenty years, and he now could not get it down again, even if he wanted to. But he did not want to get it down because he maintained that he was holding up the prestige of his country and the universe. I did not like Ramchandra at all. But the man undoubtedly had brains.

I met him about a week after my breakfast with the Pandit. Of course the Pandit had asked me to

come again next morning and I was fully determined to do so.

But it was a week before I could pay another
visit to the tank. When I did so I found that the
Pandit was, as usual, boiling his pot and I noticed
some fruit on a banana leaf set beside the tree root
on which he sat his guests. At first I had the flattering thought that this had been laid out each day for
the past week in anticipation of my visit. But then
I saw a man reach down and search among the
pile with a long skinny hand until he found a custard-apple. His other hand was up above his head,
drooping at the wrist from a withered and exactly
vertical arm.

He was a lean man with a sharp face and a small
shapeless moustache. He wore a loin-cloth that
came over his knees and large boat-like slippers
with an ornament of gold thread. He had a very
meticulous turban, a strange thing because only
princes and Indians in foreign films tie their turbans
with care. The rest are deliberately slap-dash. It
gave him a theatrical air, which was made more pro-
nounced by his dramatic skyward gesture.

I disliked this arm more and more as I studied

it. The brown skin had gone grey and the flesh had dried down to the sinews. These knotted and bulged in unnatural places and the mechanics of their join to the bones and the elbow socket could be followed as though in a diagram. The hand, as I have said, hung from the wrist in a limp gesture of farewell, but what was disconcerting was that it turned as the fakir moved his shoulders, pointing with long uncut fingernails now in this direction, now in that.

"Ah, there you are at last," said the Pandit when he saw me. He rapidly wiped some wood smuts off his face with a tail of his skirt, did the same with his right hand and came forward to greet me.

"Where have you been all these days? I was so disappointed when you didn't keep your promise to come the next morning. So was Big Tim," (for the sake of clarity I shall continue to use that name although, of course, the Pandit did not). "We felt that perhaps you didn't quite like our little community. Still, here you are, so you can't think too badly of us. Better late than never."

I apologised. "I didn't think it was so long since I was last here. I've been busy and . . ."

"Six days exactly," said the Pandit. There was no timeless peace in the tank. There is no timeless peace anywhere in India save in books: but in any case the tank was the last place to expect it. With the constant departures and arrivals of fakirs to and from festivals all over India, the Pandit and the other residents had as sharp a sense of the calendar as a busy bishop.

"But never mind," the Pandit went on and drawing me closer as he held my hand, he lowered his voice and said: "As a matter of fact, you couldn't have come at a better time. I've got Ramchandra Ghose. He only came last night and he's dropped in first thing this morning to have a chat. I'm really quite honoured." He lowered his voice still further. "He's a really big gun. The Maharajah of B . . . . . won't do a thing without his advice. He's a bit autocratic but don't mind that. He's a self-made man, you know. He was a railway clerk grade two when he had a Call. So he went on the road and—well, come and meet him."

The Pandit pushed me forward and said:

"Ramchandra, this is the gentleman that I was saying made such an impression on all of us. I'm so

glad he has the chance of meeting a man like yourself. When he goes back to England he will be able
to tell them what a really great fakir is like."

Ramchandra swivelled sharply on his tree root,
his skyward hand swivelling with him, and both he
and his hand gave me a long scrutiny.

"What is your name?"

He had the accent and the rising inflection of the
babu, which is bred from speaking English in the
tones of voice used for all Indian languages that have
a Sanskrit root. I should say at once that the babu's
way of speaking is funny only to those who do not
use their ears but take their opinions from others.
There is nothing funny in it: but it can be a very
impertinent and even insulting way of speaking.
It is perhaps fortunate for many a hot-tempered
and proud Bengalee clerk that the English never
listened to babu's English except to find material
for another good story. There is no need to re-
produce his grammatical errors here: but the tone—
off-hand, indifferent, preoccupied and yet with a
perpetual undercurrent of contempt—should be
borne in mind.

I told him my name. He turned away to his

fruit, his hand aloft bending forward as he stooped to pick up another custard-apple, like a giraffe with a stiff neck. He made no sign of acknowledgement to me until he dexterously burst the custard-apple by holding it between his knees and manipulating it with his healthy hand. Then he spoke:

"What is this I am hearing about you being from England?" He gave me a sharp look as though to catch me out in a lie.

"I was born there."

He ate some custard-apple quickly.

"You are an important man?"

"Not at all."

"Many friends?"

"A few."

"*How* many did you say?"

I found this offensive. I said:

"A lot."

"I thought you said a few. You did: but if they are highly placed and prominent celebrities—" he paused. He turned away his eyes as though seeing something in the far distance. His hand continued to stare at me.

"Do you know the Maharajah of B . . . . .?" This question took me completely by surprise, so swiftly did he shoot it at me from the depths of what I had thought was an abstraction.

"I've heard of him." I hoped that I would not be pressed to go further by this extraordinarily inquisitive man. What I had heard about the Maharajah of B . . . . . would not be likely to please his favourite fakir. But I seemed to have satisfied both Ramchandra and his doppelgänger, the wizened and questing hand in the air. Ramchandra turned away and said:

"Come and sit. Here." He nodded to a tree root beside him and I unwillingly went and sat on it. Ramchandra, for all his bare torso and weak moustache, had a compelling—an intimidating—way about him.

"So, now. You know who *I* am?"

He looked at me, giving me his attention, in a self-satisfied way. Over his head his hand peered at me with the concentration of all its four bunched fingers.

The Pandit, who was sitting on an opposite tree root came tripping into the conversation with the air of a hostess putting in the right word to make everybody comfortable.

"Oh yes, of course he does. Your fame has travelled a great deal further than you thing, Ramchandra."

Ramchandra looked at him with an expression which said that this was scarcely possible.

"I know," I said, "that the Maharajah of B . . . . . will do nothing without your advice."

"You heard that in England?"

"Yes," said the Pandit eagerly, "he did."

"Good. There is a woman called Annie Besant," Ramchandra went on. "The Maharajah wrote to her about me. She had some position in spiritual circles. The Maharajah instructed her to arrange a tour for me. England first: then America. But . . ."

He swung sharply away from me, making a click of disgust with his tongue and his teeth. I looked up to see what had irritated him and I found that it was Big Tim.

The huge man stood at the edge of the clearing, wrapped in his tentlike robe and holding a violet envelope between his massive fore-finger and thumb. When he caught the fakir's stare, he opened his mouth to say something but found no words. He waved the letter with a sheepish gesture.

"Ah yes," said the Pandit, also showing a little irritation. "I forgot. Big Tim's got a letter that he can't quite make out. Neither can I. It's a woman's handwriting. It's in Bengali and that's not one of the scripts that I'm particularly good at. So I suggested he might ask you," he said to Ramchandra.

"If you don't mind being troubled," said Big Tim very humbly.

-The great man not only minded being troubled, he made no attempt to conceal it.

"I was talking."

"Oh. I'll come back," said Big Tim, tucking the letter away out of sight in his mantle.

I got up to shake Big Tim's hand. I was sorry to see him so mortified, and made my greeting as warm as possible.

Big Tim smiled. He gave me a salutation with folded hands and seemed about to say something, when the fakir, with a most unmannerly, 'Tsk! tsk!' said:

"Well, where is the letter? Let us not waste any more time on the matter. Give it me."

I observed that the fakir's vanity was at work. It had been wounded by my putting him, even so briefly, out of the centre of the picture. He put himself back into it without delay.

Big Tim came forward and when he had settled himself on a root—as ponderous a business as lowering a foundation stone—he passed across the violet envelope.

Ramchandra took it, clamped it between his bony knees as he had done with the custard-apple. He took out a folded sheet of note-paper. As he unfolded this with his single hand, a snapshot fell out of it. I picked it up. It showed Big Tim in the midst of one of his processions of naked fakirs. He looked very fine and as solemn as a Viceroy.

"It's a woman." This from Ramchandra who was skimming the letter, moving his lips as he read.

"She thinks you're a fine fellow."

Big Tim made a deprecating movement with his hand.

"She saw you in Bombay."

"Last month that must have been. But we were only allowed in the suburbs," said Big Tim.

"Then she must have travelled a long way to

have the *privilege* of seeing you," said Ramchandra
with more than a touch of sarcasm. "She lives on
Malabar Hill,"—(a most exclusive neighborhood)—
"she's a doctor's daughter: she has travelled in
Europe: she likes moving pictures. Do you know
what they are? Never mind whether you do or you
don't. The point is that she likes you and she wants
your autograph. Put it in the bottom left hand corner and send it back to the silly little woman. That's
all." With several expert flicks of his hand he got
the letter back into its envelope and handed it to
Big Tim. I had kept the photograph and, by way
of the Pandit, I now sent it back to join the letter
in Big Tim's clumsy hands.

He studied the photograph with naïve delight,
as he had no doubt been doing since the letter arrived. He admired his own physique. He said, pointing to one of his companion fakirs in the picture:
"Just look at Das: he's got so skinny he's only fit
to frighten babies, not make 'em," and he was all
praise for the young lady who had taken the photograph; he could not have thought her cleverer had
she invented instantaneous photography herself,
which, perhaps, he thought she had. His pleasure

had only one cloud and that was a figure in the foreground who appeared to be bigger than he was. I soon explained the principles of perspective to him in a manner suitable to his mind—that is to say in about half-a-dozen words, and his serenity returned. He borrowed my fountain pen, signed the picture with a holy symbol and at my suggestion gave it to me to post.

Ramchandra watched and listened to all this with an expression of cynical amusement.

"And I wonder what holy man is next going to capture the attention of the public?" he asked. "No doubt the Pandit here who has performed the astonishing feat of self-discipline of eating only three meals a day for twenty-eight years. Or my Maharajah might try. God knows he needs some popularity. He has not got out of bed before noon for an even longer period of years. He should not be so modest. With a record like that he only needs a dab of cow-dung and ash to have all the young women in India writing to him."

This was bare-faced rudeness. It made me uncomfortable. But my discomfort was nothing to that of the other two fakirs. The Pandit wilted: Big

Tim hung his head like a bull dropping his head to the matador's sword.

"We cannot all be great Yogis," said the Pandit, but with no fight in him. "There's . . . room for everybody in our calling, after all."

"Yes, but not for the *lazy*," snapped the great fakir. "Not now. Now we are a free nation and the eyes of the world are upon us. The world expects us to give it spiritual leadership. And how many of us are prepared to answer that call? Not ten. Not five. Where would things be if I hadn't practised this extremely inconvenient posture and got it going perfectly for the glory of God?"

"No, but I couldn't, I just couldn't," said the Pandit distressfully. "I have tried it and I cannot even hold my arm up for an hour. My mind wanders. And concentration is the important thing."

"The important thing," said Ramchandra, speaking in passionate vernacular, "is the Will. That and a sense of High Calling."

"I don't suppose you'd say I'd got *that*," said Big Tim. "Would you?"

"No," said Ramchandra.

"No," agreed Big Tim. "I like to do a kind turn if I can. That's all."

"And in doing your good turn," said Ramchandra, his eyes glittering with the contempt he forced into the words, "do you ever think that you are debasing the noblest, loftiest, most difficult calling that our nation has to show, to the level of women's fancies and old crone's superstitions?"

"No, never," said Big Tim without a hint of guile or worry. "No. I can't truly say it ever crossed my mind. I just . . ." words failed him and he made a helpless gesture that indicated the feckless way he pursued his profession, and his shame that he should do so.

"You,"—I jumped, for Ramchandra, and more terribly, the fakir's hand, had turned their attention upon me. "You come from England. What have you heard there about us? You have heard that we are freaks, fakes, circus monsters, beggars, figures of fun, half-wits and perverts? Am I right?"

I nodded, not from any courageous desire to tell the truth, but because it was impossible to tell such a man that he was wrong.

"Then you can go back and tell them that although there are *some* like that—you can't deny it—" he said, looking squarely upon the Pandit and Big Tim in turn, "there's a different sort." He, if that had been possible, would have looked squarely at himself. Instead he looked up into the branches of the banyan tree.

The Pandit took his cue.

"You should tell him how you hold up the Universe," he said sycophantically. I laughed, but fortunately not too much, for the phrase was no joke: not, at least to the great fakir, who without needing any further prompting, set about telling me the story of his life.

He had been, as I have already said, a railway clerk. He freely admitted it. He said it two or three times, as though one could scarcely be expected to grasp so improbable a statement at first hearing.

"Yet even then, I wasn't just an ordinary clerk. I was ambitious. I knew my own worth and I knew my own will-power."

He glared hypnotically at me. But he had a less terrifying effect upon me than before. I had placed his moustache. It was, in those days, almost a badge of office among the lower clerical station-staff.

[164]

"But my boss was one of the easy-going type. The sort that let the English rule us for two hundred years. The sort that means well but just can't take any trouble."

The two other fakirs shifted uneasily, but Ramchandra had no intention of diverting the conversation any further from himself, and he spared them any further strokes.

"When I wanted to improve things a little, when I took new ideas to him that might have made his career in the Service, he always said 'impossible.' In those days I used to read a lot of those books about great men and how to learn from them and be a success. I read one which said that Napoleon said that the word wasn't in his dictionary. Well it was in my boss' dictionary and it was about the only one of the whole vocabulary that he used. I wish Napoleon had worked under my boss. Maybe he wouldn't have had to wait for Wellington to meet his Waterloo."

The books he mentioned silt up every bookstall in India: they are mostly written by Americans. They are read voraciously by just such a young man as Ramchandra had been. A railway clerk

has exceptional advantages in reading such literature for he can get the whole range free on the station platform.

"But if those books didn't teach me how to im-
press my boss, they taught me to recognise my
greatest quality. And that is, of course, my tremendous power of will."

He had tested his will by copying fakirs that he
had seen at festivals. There was nothing which they
could do that he could not—or so he said—and he
had had plenty of time to do it.

"I'd told my boss once and for all that he would
have to run his office without me. I walked out
of his room and he was too lazy to stop me. Then I
began really working on my will-power. I practised doing unpleasant things just to test myself.
One day I saw a Yogi with his two arms raised in
an attitude of prayer. He stood like that all morning
without so much as a tremble of the hands. Very
clever!" said Ramchandra quizzically, looking up at
his own immobile arm that had not trembled for
twenty years.

"I asked him why he did it and he said, 'If you
can hold one of your arms for three hours as I

have held both of mine for six, you will be fit to ask me that question. You will be on your way to understanding the secret of wisdom.' I went home and after a week's practise held up my arm not for three but for thirty hours. By that time the Yogi had gone on his travels but there was an old hermit who lived in the hills near my town that everybody said was a Guru and a saint. So I went to him. How easily youth is deceived. Well, I went to him with my arm already raised above my head. I bowed and touched his feet but he did not even take the trouble to look at me. I said, 'Master, do you see my arm? I can hold it in that position for twenty years if need be. What is the secret of wisdom?' He made no sign, and since he was very old I thought he might be deaf so I repeated my question a bit more loudly. Then this charlatan got up, turned his back on me, bent down nearly double and said: 'You see this backside? I've sat on it sixty-eight years.' Then he turned his face round to me and winked.

"I knew at once the sort of 'yogi' I was dealing with: the lazy type, the idlers, the men who have no respect for their profession, and I saw clearly from that very day where my duty lay. It was to rescue the whole brotherhood of Indian Yogi's from the corruption and decay that had set in. Will, will, will, *Will*! That's what we wanted. Will to do, to improve, to progress, the will to do the impossible for the sake not of yourself nor of your friends, but first for your country and then for all Mankind! That was my vision!"

"Did you," I said, "go on keeping your arm up?"

"Not all at once. I tried other austerities. I experimented. But every time I allowed my arm to sink back to a common or garden position, I seemed to hear voices saying, 'No, Ramchandra; no, no. What are you doing, O beloved, letting down your arm? What are you letting down?'

"Were they spirit voices?" I asked.

"Who knows where they came from?" But Ramchandra conveyed in his tone and manner that the man who did not was a fool. He obeyed them. He became a fully-fledged Yogi, and he set out on the first of the pilgrimages that every Yogi must make.

What happened during the first few of these pilgrimages I do not remember. Ramchandra told me, and at length, and I have no doubt his pilgrimages were a series of spiritual and personal triumphs. At any rate, the Maharajah of B . . . . . soon heard of him and invited him to his state, as he invited every celebrity he heard about: an amiable foible which ruined his state. This was the same Maharajah of B . . . . (the 84th and last) who gave a wedding feast for his favourite dog when she was mated, to which he invited his Court, the English Resident, and, as religion demanded, a great concourse of Brahmins and fakirs.

"The Maharajah came to see my arm," said Ramchandra. "He stayed to listen to *me*."

The Maharajah, I gathered, had received at one tremendous buffet all the tricks of getting on, impressing, influencing and browbeating that Ramchandra had gathered from his bookstall reading. Ramchandra knew when his moment had arrived, and he took it. But it seemed that the Maharajah stood his ground under the merciless hail of psychological weapons until Ramchandra did something which I doubt whether he ever found in a book. He told one lie, so tremendous, so barefaced, and so utterly incredible that—as so often happens—he laid the Maharajah flat on his back. The Maharajah of

B . . . . . asked him why he held up his arm and Ramchandra said:

"Because if I let it down the Universe will come tumbling about my ears."

I say it was a lie. But I have no reason whatever to think that Ramchandra did not believe it to be the plain truth. Few people, after all, who have come to a conclusion about their relation to the Infinite ever admit that they might have been wrong.

As for Ramchandra, he had the proof pat. So had the Pandit, who obviously enjoyed this socially successful part of his friend's career and who, in any case, liked talking about Maharajahs. It was he who interrupted Ramchandra's tirade and it was he who explained the Master's Proof. I am glad he did, for had he left it to Ramchandra I am sure I would never have grasped it, any more than a rabbit would grasp a philosophical lecture delivered by a snake.

"You see," said the Pandit in his most persuasive barrister's voice, "the Purpose of the Universe is the Improvement of Man. Brahma, who is the Creator and the Destroyer, who is the *IS*, so to speak, conceived the Universe one day while turning his head from left to right. This was the first movement he had made for several million years and he made it because he was bored. He therefore thought of the idea of making Man and providing him with all that was necessary for Man to become like the gods. Now to do that, as everybody knows, one must rise superior to the senses. You follow me—or do you disagree?"

"No, no," said Ramchandra, impatiently, "he doesn't disagree. Go on, go on, do."

"Well, nobody can deny that Ramchandra has mastered his senses. So he is in a way, a god. Now the gods control the Universe: and if a god falls, the whole Universe is changed. Therefore Ramchandra really cannot let his arm down. Well, what do you think of that?"

I thought it nonsense. But I did not say so. It did not seem any sillier than many other proofs of our importance in the scheme of things. And at least Ramchandra was content with holding up his own arm. He did not demand that everybody else hold theirs up, too.

"The Maharajah," said the Pandit, "was so impressed that he came to talk to Ramchandra every day. In the end he made him his unofficial Prime Minister and that's what he is today."

Ramchandra nodded. Then, with the perfect seriousness with which he made every statement, he said:

"The Maharajah told me that he tried every other way of running the State and they had all broken down because his Ministers were so dishonest. 'At least with you,' he told me, 'I can be sure you've only got one hand in the Privy Purse, not both, like the others.' It was a humourous remark and you should not get the impression that the Prince thinks I would ever rob him. I am not interested in money. What I ask of people is not that they pay me but that they have *faith*."

"What faith?" I asked.

"Faith in the fact that our great nation has known the secret of leading the world to salvation since the dawn of time," he said. "Faith in *this*." He pointed to his withered arm and his eyes blazed. "Faith that this will save you and the rest of suffering humanity: faith that this does save you every minute from being hurled to destruction in a torrent of flame. Faith that in this and *nothing else*, lies safety."

"Do you really mean *nothing* else?" said Big Tim, stirring uneasily.

"That is what I said."

"But—well—Balan, for instance? He sits on nails."

Ramchandra sniffed, cleared his throat and spat, in an annihilating expression of contempt.

"Yes, I know. It's very ordinary," said Big Tim, heavily. "Still . . ."

"You cannot just *invent* a faith to suit yourself," said Ramchandra. "You cannot get salvation by sitting on nails because you happen to have a leathery backside. What does everyone in this country do who likes an easy life but wants to be thought holy? Go to the carpenter, get a few nails hammered into a board, lower themselves gingerly on to it for a few minutes each day, till they learn the trick."

"It's not to fidget," said the Pandit.

"They think they've got heavenly grace," said the Master, "when they can do it all day long. But they haven't got grace, they've got callouses."

[173]

Big Tim sighed. "I'm sure you must be right. But it seems strange that there's only *one* way of being holy."

"Though for some Indians, of course," said the Master, with his terrible sarcasm, "even getting calloused is too much trouble."

And having launched this all-destroying thunderbolt, he rose and left us, taking, to my unexpressible relief, his holy arm with him.

The morning was spoiled. Big Tim got up immediately afterwards, saying that his sect always took baths on this particular day and he went off to wallow, conspicuously praying, in the waters of the tank.

My friend the Pandit chattered in a desultory fashion but soon he began fiddling with a devotional book made of dried palm leaves threaded together with string. He flapped over the leaves once or twice without looking on them: then he started reading in earnest. I saw that he was going through his prayers, a thing he had never done before. Feeling that I was not wanted in this new serious atmosphere, I silently said goodbye, and left.

GARDENING NOTES

I LEFT BOTH INDIA AND ENGLAND and retired to a
place half-way betweeen. Here (in Italy) I found
a house by the sea with three terraces, one of vines,
one of oranges, and one of olives. I lived in peace
and thought much about the question that my ex-
periences had raised. I know patriotism to be a
good and virtuous thing, but I had seen it make men
absurd. Meantime, I cultivated my garden.

* * * * *

The nearest large town to my garden is Naples.
On top of a hill in Naples is a vast white monastery
and in the monastery a bronze bust. It shows the
philosopher Campanella. On the base of the statue
is a plaque. This shows Campanella again, but he is
naked, and bound. He is straddled over a devilish
machine that is tearing his flesh with hooks. Three

Inquisitors sit at a table, debating with him in his agony.

The question they were debating was, in part, whether or not the earth goes round the sun. Copernicus, who was not long dead, had said that it did. Campanella, although no scientist, agreed with him. The Inquisitors thought that it did not; alternatively, if it did, Campanella should not say so in public because in their opinion Campanella had no respect for the beliefs of religious people.

There was right on both sides. Campanella was right concerning the earth. The Inquisitors were right concerning Campanella's contempt for religion. There was also wrong on both sides. The Inquisitors would not increase Campanella's love for the Church by slowly tearing his flesh. Campanella did not see that the earth would still go round the sun whether he said it did or whether he denied it. He was not suffering for science but for his idea of how men should think: and his opinion was that men should think as scientists tell them, or be imprisoned.

The scene portrayed is, in a word, a typically human one.

This is how Campanella, who was also a fine poet describes his torture and twelve years of his imprisonment:—

"The earth drank six pounds of my blood . . .
My limbs were seven times torn;
I was cursed at by fools and forced to listen to
their fables;
The sun was denied to my eyes;
The fibres of my nerves were wrenched; my bones
broken;
My flesh was beaten into pulp.
Raw fear, blood, manacles and a little filthy food—
This was my daily lot."

There can be no reader of these words that does not feel horror at this man's fate, and, at the best, pity for the men who made him suffer it. With that horror, and with the pity, there may be a sense of relief: for our spirits have escaped from at least one foul dungeon. We no longer make a man ride upon hooks because his view of God does not coincide with ours. Certainly, men are still tortured for their beliefs. The dungeons of the Inquisition would not hold the number of people that had been sentenced during the single day in which I have written this page: but not even the barbarian at our gates dare punish them for their religion. They must be tortured for other crimes—treason to a party, dealing in foreign exchange, spying for America, and they must be made to confess these offences lest people think they are being punished for being a Cardinal, a Protestant missionary or a Jew. We have advanced. There is no less persecution in the world: but there is one less reason for it.

It is worth pausing a moment to see how this came about. Men do not get better at such a giddy rate that we can afford to take any softening of their savagery for granted.

Protestants and Catholics fought the bloodiest war in European history and they fought it for thirty terrible years. Their quarrel is still not settled. A Prostestant is not a Catholic, and a Catholic cannot worship in a Protestant church without offending against his faith. He cannot even marry a Protestant unless she, in however summary a fashion, agrees that in the issue between them, his church is right and his children will be told so. But although we sometimes feel that there is no cause too absurd for men to refrain from killing one another over it, on reflection we must agree that this one is. There will never be another war between Protestants and Catholics: there will never even be a sizeable massacre. If this state of affairs was not achieved by both sides agreeing, nor by one side surrendering, then it must have been brought about by something quite outside the quarrel itself.

Let us put aside immediately that it was brought about by commonsensical people who cared not a rap for either party. Intelligent neutrals do not stop wars of that sort. There are innumerable people in India who are neither practising Hindus nor believing Mohammedans, but not five years ago trains pulled in to Indian platforms with blood streaming from their footboards and the passengers sitting each neatly in a corner, without their heads. Mohammedans and Indians had fought and perhaps a million people had died. That madness passed. No one knows how: but it was certainly not because cool neutrals stood reasoning between the parties.

We know more about the end of the war between the Protestants and Catholics. That died away because the principal persons on each side were forced by the nature of their trade to have no

religion at all or—what is much the same thing—
they were forced to ignore their religion while
they were doing their job.

On both sides the war was fought with considerable military skill: some of the commanders were
among the most able men that military science has
known. These commanders were early brought to
see that if a man aimed a cannon at them the issue
of whether the shot would carry far enough to
blow off their heads was settled not by the religious
beliefs of the gunner, but by his experience in shooting, the construction of his cannon, and the quality
of his gunpowder. Both sides were convinced that
they were fighting Anti-Christ. But both sides
slowly learned that if, for instance, the captains of
the Whore of Babylon knew how to handle their
cavalry wing and had enough of them to handle,
they often won, in spite of their superstitious beliefs: and if the gunners of the Abomination of
Desolation had a good supply of English bronze
cannon, then, like as not they would stand in such
holy places as took their fancy.

English cannon and well-trained cavalry cost
money. Money came, as it always comes, from

doing business: business in the Thirty Years War came to a stop. The only sort of trade that was done in whole areas of Europe was of an unprofitable nature. To take only one instance out of many hundreds, when the Duke of Saxe-Weimar besieged Briarch, one of the inhabitants traded a diamond ring for three pounds of bread and a glass of wine. Those without diamond rings ate one another.

Such a state of affairs would not stop most wars. If a war is about trade (and many wars are) one side might well consider it a patriotic duty to eat rats and an inevitable austerity to eat one another, and they might well pursue that course to the last rat and the last man. But with this war things were different. Men cannot very well kill one another for an *idea* if they are constantly thinking about something which is not that idea at all. To revert for the moment to Campanella, the Inquisitors would scarcely have been as persistent in their persecution if they had been forced to beg their daily meals from door to door: and the plan behind their seating Campanella on his hooks was to divert his mind if only for a short period from its obsession with his scientific Utopia. In a conflict of ideas, several centuries—he read the Bible with his wits about him. The awkward questions which he asked did not shake the Church: but they shook a great number of its priests. By the time they had copied Voltaire and really read the book that they preached from, and by the time that they had hammered out some satisfactory answers, they had forever lost exclusive hold on men's minds and, in the nineteenth century, came perilously near to losing their hold upon men's souls as well. When, a few years ago, I considered that I had reached that age at which I could with confidence adopt and follow the Christian faith, and when I enquired of both Protestant and Catholic priests for guidance, they did not try to convince me that Christianity was true: they laboured to show me that it was not absurd.

We call the age of Voltaire, and of Gibbon and David Hume, the Age of Enlightenment. We are still living in it. The principal belief of the Age of Enlightenment was that a man can attain his greatest happiness by the free exercise of his reason. What satisfies his reason he must do: what does not satisfy it, he must dismiss. It was an attractive idea. Unfortunately among the things which have satis-

But we stand in danger of once again entering a conflict with the notion that we have invisible but all conquering allies. The invisible ally that the Protestants relied on was God: the invisible ally that sustained the Catholics was also God. It turned out that God was a non-belligerent. Now we believe that we enter the conflict sustained not only by the rightness of our cause but by our national virtues—our American energy, our British pluck, our Russian fortitude in tribulation. Just as the Catholic believed that when he aimed his gun it was not only he who trained the sights, but all the less pacific saints assisted by the holy archangels; just as the Protestant believed that it was not only his horse that would carry him irresistibly through the ranks of the enemy but also Divine Providence, so we believe that we shall not be merely Pfc. Smith and General Jones and Commissar Ivanov and Infantryman Vanilyvitch, but something much bigger and more certain because we were born not only fallible human beings but men strong in national virtues. That is why we grow so angry when an Englishman aims to make a bomb for the Russians, and a Russian attempts to get across a frontier to help the military intelligence of the Americans. No Catholic could have fought happily if he had felt that St. Michael might at any moment have developed Lutheran leanings, nor could the Protestant have been easy in his mind if he had suspected that Divine Election had chosen, for once, the Pope.

But suppose that our belief in our national virtues is exaggerated. Suppose that the British have no more fortitude under bombardment than the Ukrainians: suppose that the Americans are not mysteriously born with a better knowledge of mechanical engineering than the Russians: suppose that the Russians turn and run like lesser men when they are beaten? Suppose that Mother Nature, too, is non-belligerent? Then one thing is certain. The side which discovers first the truth will be the side that will win.

AN ANSWER

WHAT IS THE TRUTH? If you will stay with me for a page or two more, I shall give an answer.

There are no national virtues. We are alone, each one of us. If we are good, we are good ourselves. If we are bad, the virtues of others will not make us better. We cannot borrow morals. They are ours or they do not exist for us.

This is a very terrible answer and we try to avoid it. Each of us seeks some way of magnifying himself. We seek to inflate ourselves: we want to achieve the size we think we should be, but without trouble. We want to avoid the responsibility that we have to ourselves alone. There is no way of avoiding it. A nation cannot make our souls for us.

Neither can any group. In this cold age we have a great faith in groups. But this faith may betray us. If ten people sit round a table and find themselves in agreement, nine are merely admiring their own sagacity and one man is doing the thinking. This does not change as the group gets larger. We here in Europe have learned that very bitterly. We have said, "We are doing fine." "We are jolly good fellows." "We are getting things done." Then suddenly one day some of us became "they." Then came the knock on the door in the small hours, the covered truck, and the rubber truncheon.

We cannot take refuge in a political idea. The man who becomes a Communist does not add a cubit to his stature, although he thinks he does. To live in a free land does not lessen our responsibility to ourselves. A narrow, bad man is not made any less narrow, or any less bad, by the freedom of his institutions. Every mouse was perfectly free to express his opinion as to who should bell the cat. One was elected by universal secret suffrage. When the election was over, they were still mice.

Or you may have accepted, as I have, the moral discipline of a great church. That does not make either you or me any less responsible for our own souls. Nobody can help us, in the end. We cannot say: "I did so-and-so because my neighbour, who agrees with my religious views, did the same."

You are asked to love your neighbour as yourself: you are not called upon to share his opinions. He may be a Pharisee.

Nor can you take refuge in your caste or your class. I have shown where that leads. But I began by saying that all sensible men are agreed that to love one's country is a noble thing. Is this proved wrong because we must make our own souls? Not in the least. It is a noble love when it is honest, because when it is honest it is a discipline. First, it teaches us to obey the laws. This we must do because all men are created equal in at least one thing: not one of them is to be trusted to rule the rest unless he is restrained by law. And if he is not restrained by it, our discipline teaches us to disobey him and reestablish the rule of law according to the traditions of our native land. Secondly, it disciplines us in our dealings with other countries, provided it is a true patriotism and not a false one.

A false patriotism is that which makes us love not our country but the ideas that have been put into our minds about it, and thus about ourselves. A true patriotism is a simpler thing. It is to love the land of one's birth: its hills and mountains, cities and skies: its sea; its air; its language and the people who nurtured you. It reminds us constantly not of our greatness, but of our true size. We were not born across a continent or bred at a straddle between boundaries. We were born in a place, a house, a town, a village. We did not have a hundred million fathers and mothers. We had one father and one mother. We were not taught that right and wrong were things to be debated daily by diplomats. We were taught what they were by a handful of people, and we were taught that they did not change.

The man who has lost this love has lost himself. He has no measuring rod. It is he who joins the Party. The man who keeps this love can face the world with great confidence. He knows that however vast the decision he is called upon to make, when he decides between a matter of right and wrong, he must be no bigger than his breeches.

AN EPILOGUE IN
WARNING

"Cervius," says Horace, "haec inter vicinus garrit anilis ex re fabellas." That is, "Now and then our neighbour Cervius rattles off old wives' tales that fit the case."

I would exercise the same privilege now that I have come to the end.

* * * * *

The greatest King of India in India's Golden Age was Rama (so it is said).

When Rama was a young man and still only a prince he would often walk to the top of a hill that overlooked his native city of Ayodha. He would gaze down at the shining city spread out at his feet and his heart would swell with pride that he belonged to it.

On top of the hill was a pillar, and on top of the pillar was some writing, but Rama could never make out its meaning because it was so old and battered.

He mentioned this at his father's court and his question was passed from one official to another until it arrived at the right one. This was the King's Remembrancer, an old man with a silvery voice and a great fondness for hearing it.

He gladly went with Rama to the top of the hill. He made a few commonplace remarks to test the timbre of his voice and finding it perfect, he began:—

* * * * *

First he made the traditional invocation to the Gods, which he did in these words:

"Hail, O Gods: grant me a silver tongue and listeners with brains between their ears."

After which he told this story.

"You must first know," he said, "that our people were not always here. They came—and I speak of long ago—from a cold country beyond the mountains. That is why our women have fair skins and we men are no darker than old ivory. That is also the reason that we look down on men who are darker than ourselves and find them ugly."

"Why?" asked Rama. "Why do we find them ugly?"

"Because," said the King's Remembrancer, "the complexion that comes from a cold climate is clearly more beautiful than the complexion which comes from a hot one."

"In that case," said Rama, "we should think that red noses are very elegant, but I do not think we do. But go on with your story."

"When our people came down the snow mountain," the Remembrancer said, "they were led by King Yagu, who was the wisest man who ever lived. They emerged, with King Yagu at their head, from a gloomy pass and found themselves among hills that each commanded vast prospects of a smiling plain. But the hills and the valleys between them were very stony. Instantly some among the company fell to work. Some fetched rocks and began to build a fort, some felled trees to make house posts, others dug holes in which to put them, and still others built a fire and brought water from a spring. But King Yagu stood aside and did nothing.

"When they had built the wall to the height of a man's knee, the leader of the men who had done the building came to King Yagu and said, 'Sire, bless this wall, for here we have water, a dry place for our houses, and a view which seems to us to be that of Paradise, while the climate is mild beyond anything we have ever known. Here we shall stay and here we shall live.'

"King Yagu replied, 'The view is certainly very fine: but what is a fine view to a man whose eyes are turned inwards to his belly? What will you eat?'

"To which the man replied, 'We shall plough these hills and dig the valleys and we shall grow our food. It will be hard at first but that is as it should be. We are none of us afraid of hard work: it does us good and we enjoy it. Besides, it will keep us strong and healthy in this very soft climate.'

" 'Very well,' said King Yagu. 'Let those who

love hard work stay here. Let those who do not go with me.' Then he blessed the wall. Some fifty men and their families stayed behind. The rest followed Yagu, although they felt somewhat guilty in doing so. But King Yagu praised them and encouraged them and led them into the plains.

"There they came upon a green and happy land which was as pleasant as it had seemed from the hills, except for its inhabitants who were exceedingly black—a colour," said the King's Remembrancer catching himself up and bowing towards Prince Rama, "—a colour which personally I think most becoming provided one approaches the matter with an open mind. However," he went on, "these people, in spite of their complexion were extremely unpleasant. They allowed our people to rest for one day but gave them to understand with angry looks and spear thrusts that they would not be allowed to stay, or even to proceed without making a heavy payment. They allowed them to pitch their camp on some fields by a river. The fields were soft with fine grass and innumerable flowers, the river ran between banks of glistening sand and the climate was both mild and bracing, a wonderful state of affairs which has quite disappeared in our less happy age. Now some of the cleverer men went bathing and very soon discovered that the sands of the river glistened because they were sown with small gold nuggets. They therefore hurried off to the black men and began negotiating with them. Next morning King Yagu awoke to find them busily putting up houses of reeds and poles, and he was told that they had been so fortunate as to make a treaty with the black men. The negotiators said that this treaty undoubtedly called for considerable payments in the years to come. This would have to be made in food, drink, iron, wood, coral beads and several other expensive goods. But if everybody set about getting the gold from the river, and if everybody agreed to pay one quarter of it in tax, they would be able to buy these things or hire strangers to make them and so discharge their payment to the black men, who seemed quite unaware of the riches lying at their feet. All that remained was for King Yagu to give the treaty his blessing.

"King Yagu said, 'Have you told the black men that they have infinite riches underneath their feet?' At which the counsellors laughed heartily, slapped their thighs and said the King was a wonderful wit. Then the King blessed the treaty and said, 'Prosper in peace. Let those who wish to live by picking up gold nuggets and pay one quarter taxes to my counsellors, do so. Let the rest come with me.'

"Very many people stayed behind but many went with the King, particularly those who had taken a dislike to the black men, and did not trust them.

"These, with King Yagu at their head, moved onward and a fine sight they made. First bold outriders on thick, stocky horses pointing the way, then the King and his Court walking or riding, then the wagons and the women, the oxen straining with their noses to the ground or clashing their wide horns as they quarrelled with their yoke-fellows, and last, gleaming and clattering, the warriors, guarding the rear.

"They were passing through the flat lands where the earth is black and the farmers take two crops a year, when they came to a great rock, a mountain almost, that shot up from the plain and had no other mountain anywhere near it, nor rock, nor even hillock, for as far as the eye could see.

"Here the warriors stopped, or most of them. Here they too asked the King to bless a town, although what they meant to build was not so much a town as a great fortress, on the top of the rock.

" 'And what will you eat?' asked the King, 'and how will you drink?'

" 'There is a spring, Sire,' they answered, 'and as for eating and any other comfort, the men who hold that fort can take what they please when they please from all this rich land around us: they can even have it carried to their gates at a clap of their hands.' Saying this they rolled their eyes and stroked their vast moustaches and made the links of their armour jingle.

" 'Very well,' said the King, 'let those who wish to live in a fortress and have a whole kingdom at their service stay here. The rest come with me.'

"So on they went, a smaller company now, and

many said they feared it was a poor one, the braver
spirits being all left behind, and only the cautious
ones going with the King. But Yagu was well
pleased and went on cheerfully for seven days more
until he came to a place where two great rivers met
and he said:

" 'Here, my children, we shall build a town.'

"So they did: and the town they built was this
town, Ayodha. As you know, it prospered. Each
year they thanked the gods for their abundance
by killing a perfectly white horse, and they thanked
the King by buying him a new wife, who if not
perfectly white was as pale as they could find.

"Then one year, just after harvest all the women
and children from the town that the hard workers
had founded, came weeping to the gates and asked
asylum. Their husbands they said, had changed the
very shape of the hills with their toil, but no amount
of hard work had been able to change the weather.
This was as mild as they had first thought, but
much more wayward. The rain was soft but always
came at the wrong time; the sun was benign but
never shone in season. The crops had failed and the

men had beaten their wives: not because their wives had anything to do with the weather but because they had formed the habit of hard physical exercise and they wished to relieve their feelings.

"The wives and children were welcomed into the city; and so too, were such of their husbands who followed them. But most of the hardworking and disappointed farmers went back to the cold lands from which they had come.

"Those who had built their town by the golden sands were not so lucky. The black men soon found out the meaning of the nuggets and they demanded more and more payments until the tax was not one quarter but three. Since the black men were on all sides of them, the settlers had no way out but to get more and more gold and do more and more trade, till their livers went wrong and their faces turned the same colour as the nuggets, and they mostly died. Some thin, yellow scarecrows turned up at Ayodha and were compassionately made welcome.

"The soldiers in the fortress were much more successful: at least they always said they were. They fought all the year round except in the monsoon. They mostly won. From time to time a party of soldiers would come from the fort to Ayodha to buy more bows and arrows and swords. If there were four of them they would muster six legs, five arms, five eyes and four ears between them. They were always unable to understand why we in this city drudged for our living when all you had to do was build a fort on top of a hill. Their castle was finally seized by your great-great-great-grandfather in payment for a debt to our guild of swordsmiths whom they had not paid for seventy-five years.

"When King Yagu had reigned for a quarter of a century the people, who were now very rich, gave him an elephant with tusks bound in gold and an ivory howdah studded with gems. When he had accepted this they asked him to explain how he had known that their companions should be left behind, but the King did not answer them immediately. Instead he caused this pillar to be set up. If Your Highness will look up to the top of it, you will see that once—though time and the sand in the May wind has smoothed almost all away—there was writing.'

" 'I have often observed it,' said Rama, 'but I have never made out what it said.'

" 'I shall tell you,' said the King's Remembrancer. 'It said: *Pause, Stranger, and look upon Ayodha. Here we can afford every luxury, save enthusiasm*'."